Shootin' The Breeze

Cowboy Style

Dedicated to

Harry W. Olson
The Best Cowman I Know

Shootin' the Breeze

Cowboy Style

by

Ken Overcast

BVP

Bear Valley Press

Ken Overcast is available for western entertainment.
His award winning delivery and down home connection
are a hit with audiences everywhere.
Contact information below.

Cover Painting
H. Steven Oiestad

Rear and Inside Cover B/W Photo & Coloration
John H. Warner

Illustrated by
Ben Crane

Chapter Heading Photo
Charles E. Morris

Copyright © 2005 Ken Overcast
-all rights reserved-
Library of Congress Catalogue Card Number: 2005901616
Printed in Canada
First Edition
First Printing

ISBN-13: 978-0-9718481-1-5
ISBN-10: 0-9718481-1-4

Bear Valley Press
PO Box 1542
Chinook, Montana 59523
(406) 357-3824
www.kenovercast.com

Discounts are available for bulk purchases.

"There are three things that cowboys
will just never understand;
Women, Racehorses, and Money."

Will Rogers

Photographic Credits

Table of Contents

Introduction

Charles E. Morris Photo

Roy Matheson on Honky Tom
Chinook, Montana
1904

Introduction

Thanks for cracking the cover of *Shootin' the Breeze*. I think you're going to be glad you did. If you can just imagine yourself running into two or three cowboys with a little time to kill out on a remote cow trail somewhere here in the Real West, these little tales are the sort of thing you'd be likely to hear.

Far more of these little musings are true than you might expect from a casual observation or first reading. Truth *is* stranger than fiction, you know. At least some of them were true when they happened. Since then... well, maybe there's been a little imagination applied and a little B.S. sprinkled about on occasion. One ol' boy I know prefers to call it "creative truth enhancement". If you happen to follow the government shenanigans that ooze out of Washington DC on a daily basis, and especially if you believe what you hear, then I'm sure you'll more than likely accept every word of this as the gospel truth, too.

I had a fella ask me not long ago how in the world I keep folks from beatin' the dickens out of me for telling on them like I do. Actually, I HAVE been threatened a time or two, but only a real sissy would allow mere threats of bodily harm stand in the way of telling a good story.... so much B.S., so little time. Besides, I feel it's part of my duty to mankind to spread as much baloney as possible, so bowing to intimidation is totally out of the question.

In some cases, the names have been changed to protect the parties involved (and to keep my neck from being

13

busted), and in others the tales are not only "ever' word true", but the original names have been retained just for the fun of it.

For the most part, they're the type of little stories that will tickle your funny bone. Life is just too durn serious, and they say that a good laugh now and then is good for your gizzard. You might say this book could be considered as therapeutic B.S.

I need to breifly explain a little about the picture of Roy Matheson riding the bucking horse on a preceding page. I recounted Roy's entire story in the first chapter of *Yesterday's Yarns*, so I'll not go into a lot of detail here, but it's an enthrallingly true tale about a real Montana cowboy and well worth the read. The picture was snapped by frontier photographer Charles E. Morris, and won the photography competition at the 1904 World's Fair in St. Louis.

Trust me; Roy's true story is even better than the photograph, so you know it's got to be a dandy. It's one of my very favorite pictures and epitomizes my passion.... the Real West. Mr. Morris did more than any photographer in this area for preserving the way the West really was. Historians will forever be in his debt. We're once again using that great shot as a part of every chapter heading.

If you're like me, finding the time to read a book is sometimes a challenge. I've certainly got the interest, but for some reason can't seem to squeeze out as much time as I'd like. I've got markers stuck in probably twenty books around here. Some of them I started to read so long ago, that I can't remember a thing that I've already read.

This book is different. Each little episode of *Shootin' the Breeze* stands on its own, so you can start or stop anyplace without missing out on a thing. And.... if you're really pressed for time.... just consider leavin' the book by the john. Not only is the atmosphere appropriate, but the stories are exactly the right length.... enjoy.

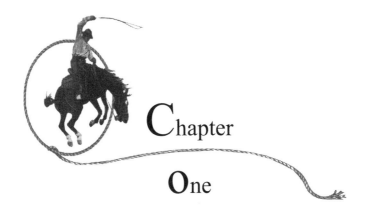

Chapter

One

Grandad's Double Uddered Cow

*I*t's not every day that you see a double-uddered milk cow.... I mean a cow with two bags, each with four spigots, one right in front of the other. In fact I would venture to say that most folks have *never* seen one. I don't believe I ever have, but there was a guy that worked for my Grandad back in the fifties that would have bet a month's pay that he did.

Of course Ol' Art was prone to hit the bottle a little hard at times, and as a result, had a tendency to see all kinds of strange things crawlin' on the bunkhouse walls when his good time was wearing off. Consequently, even though he went to his grave swearin' that what he saw was the truth, I really have my doubts that very many of the folks he told ever believed him.

Here's the story. This little deal all happened one time after Art had been out on a big toot. As was the case with

15

a lot of the hired men that worked at our place back then, about once a month he felt the deep inner need to blow all the money he had coming, plus all he could bum on wine, women, and song. It finally got so bad, that out of desperation, he had to give up singin' entirely. He never did quit the other two. A little honky-tonk dive in Harlem called Beanie's got most of everything that Art ever earned.

You see, all of this "udder confusion" actually started just because me and my cousin Eddy wanted to practice bein' cowboys. We were ten or twelve years old and everyone knows that a good cowboy can ride "anything growin' hair", and one of the things we hadn't tried yet was Grandad's old Holstein milk cow..... so give 'er a try we did.

I don't know if you've ever ridden any cows, but just in case you haven't, the traditional method of riding regular stock cows is with a bull rope. It's just like real bull ridin' only a lot easier. One look at that old milk cow's razor backbone would be enough to start any cowboy with half a brain on a quest for "Plan B". Attempting to ride a milkin' Holstein with a bull rope could have a detrimental effect on generations to come. In fact, it's very probable that the entire branch of the rider's family tree would be fatally and permanently pruned in the first couple of seconds.

Fortunately, all we needed to implement "Plan B" was a saddle. No problem.... there were several of those in the barn. It's a funny thing though, a milk cow's back and a stock saddle really don't really have that much in common. It solved the sharp backbone problem, but the fit left a little to be desired. Either the Good Lord didn't intend those critters to be saddled up, or the design boys over at the saddle shop had dropped the ball.

But, saddle her up we did. After getting the old girl roped and tied up to a post, we began strapping on our riggin'. In all fairness to our ill fated effort, if we hadn't been in such a big hurry we more than likely would have done a little better job, but our window of opportunity was closing fast.

You see, Eddy and I were there all alone and everyone else was due back home in short order. Although getting caught riding the family milk cow might not prove to be fatal, a willow switch to our saddle setting area was a distinct possibility. Grandad was a little narrow minded about some of those things.

With a horse halter and a lead rope for a buck rein, I stepped up on her. Eddy was game, but he drew the long straw. Besides, he always had more sense than I did anyway. When I got a good seat, my partner in crime snapped the breakaway hondo loose that was holding her to the post, and I stuck the spurs to her. Away we went. Because there was only one witness to my incredible ride, and he's sworn to secrecy, let me take this opportunity to assure you that it was indeed a sight to behold.

It's really too bad that the Discovery Channel film crew wasn't there. I'd have been famous right on the spot. I can still see all those good lookin' cowgirls swooning in my mind as I recall those next few seconds.

I'm not sure if I lost my seat when the saddle turned or when she jumped over the corral fence, but I do know that she got away and I wound up on the ground. The old girl busted the top two poles on the fence when she went over, and wound up gallopin' around the pasture squirting milk all over the saddle that was now turned down under her belly.

This obviously wasn't part of the plan, and it threw our time schedule off so bad that we were still chasing her around out in the cow pasture when Grandad and Art crossed the cattle guard. Ooooh boy!

Grandad had made a trip to Harlem to pick up his hired man that had used up all of his money, credit, and welcome down at Beanie's. Being in his half inebriated, half in the middle of the DTs state of mind, Art mistook the saddle under old Flossy's belly as another udder.

"Where in the dickens did joo fin' a cow with two bags?" the red-nosed shakin' old drunk slobbered. "Thasss the dangedest thing I ever ssheen!"

That's probably the way bad rumors get started. Ol' Art was absolutely certain he'd seen a double-uddered cow, and went to the grave swearin' it was so. Unfortunately, Grandad got the picture right away, and me 'n Eddy were in deep do-do.

After he got through visitin' with us about it, we decided that maybe we could make one black and white exception to our "everything growin' hair" rule.

Chapter Two

Southern Snake Bite

*I*t's really funny. Out here in the range country there are some places that the rattlesnakes are thicker 'n the dickens and then just a few miles away there aren't any at all. I guess maybe there's some things we just aren't supposed to figure out, but why they're so prolific in one place and not in others does seem a little strange. If there is anything I hate it's a snake, and anyone that's ever shared real estate with 'em has a tale or two to tell.

I was just thinkin' of a snake story that I heard about a couple of early day settlers. They had a bunch of rattlesnakes move into their root cellar. They must have dug the cellar into a hill that was either on top of the snake den, or at least close to it, and it was a real catastrophe. The poor lady of the house was from back east, and scared spit-less of snakes, while the old man was completely oblivious to her concerns.

He was lookin' for gold under every rock and was dead certain that he'd be rich at any minute, so he didn't have time to worry about a little inconvenience like a few snakes in the root cellar. He "fixed" the problem, though. The enterprising and far too busy prospector hung an old cowbell on the inside of the cellar door with the following instructions to his frightened mate:

"Shake the door a little before you go in so the bell rings, and then listen. If you don't hear a rattle go right on in. If you hear a snake in there, just take a stick with you." I'm not too sure how all that turned out, but I think maybe that remedy might stretch the marital bliss on our outfit a little. Heck, a bull snake or two in the basement can get the cook all stirred up around here.

Then there was Homer and Dolly. They lived in pretty bad snake country, and I'm not too sure you ever get really used to it. Neither one of them liked the nasty critters, but Dolly was especially afraid of them. Back in the fifties sometime they had a real scare. The indoor plumbin' that Homer had installed about ten years earlier went on the fritz. The sewer line plugged up or something, and the john didn't work anymore, but Homer was busy hayin' and didn't have time to dig the durn thing up. Besides, they still had the old biffy out by the barn, and that had worked for forty years before. He just didn't view the problem with the same degree of urgency as Dolly did.

"I'll get 'er fixed before winter sets in, but we just don't have the time right now. You gotta make hay while the sun shines."

"But the grass is tall out there, and there are snakes everyplace. That's just plain dangerous, Homer," Dolly pleaded…. to no avail.

"It's a funny thing to me that we used that ol' outhouse for forty years without gettin' snake bit. Just get the lawnmower and cut the grass around there. It'll be fine."

Dolly dutifully and very carefully cut the tall grass on both sides of the seldom used path, certain that she would be attacked by a herd of snakes at any moment, but as luck would have it, didn't see a single one. She sicked the dog on every grasshopper that buzzed, and there were sure plenty of those. The poor ol' girl was nervous as a tomcat in a room full of rockin' chairs.

The old out house was in pretty bad repair. It hadn't been used for several years, and the door was just sort of hangin' there by the top hinge. Now, Dolly really needed to use the antiquated old facility, but was trying desperately to put it off long enough to let Homer use it first. She'd make HIM be the one to make sure there weren't a bunch of snakes in there. It was almost noon, and he was due in from the hay field at anytime, but she simply couldn't wait any longer. She just had to go….**NOW**.

Brandishing an old hoe she had gotten from the garden out in front of herself like a Samurai swordsman closing in for the kill, Dolly slowly crept up to the foreboding structure. She very warily pulled the broken door completely open, keeping a sharp ear tuned for that dreadful snake rattle she was certain would begin at any moment. Nothing. She peered quickly into the corners for any of the vile reptiles that might be lurking inside, but thankfully again, came up empty.

"Thank Goodness!" Dolly thought to herself…. "No snakes!" She quickly brushed the dust from the old wooded seat and hurriedly sat down to the urgent business at hand. She had barely made it in time.

The blissful sweet relief was short lived and very abruptly interrupted by a sharp and sudden pain in the very sensitive southern end of her anatomy.

SNAKE BIT!! In the haste of the moment, she had forgotten to look IN the hole before she'd sat down. With a yell that would put a Comanche to shame, and her bloomers still around her ankles, Dolly double-hopped across the forty yards between the biffy and the mowing machine her hubby was just pullin' into the yard. Homer says he thinks she probably set some sort of a sack race record…. too bad there wasn't an official timer present.

"I've been snake bit!" she shrieked. We've got to get to the doctor!"

Now, Homer is normally a calm sort, but this **WAS** an emergency, so he loaded her right up in the their old '49 Ford and took off for town with the dust boilin' out behind them. Dolly cried hysterically for the entire twenty miles. The doctor quickly looked her over with all the due diligence of a businessman perusing his morning paper. Sure enough…. right there between the obituaries and the sports section he found a little bruise. Fortunately, he was absolutely certain it wasn't caused by a snakebite, so no further treatment was needed. Relieved by the good news, Dolly had finally settled down a little, and they headed the old Ford back home to get to the bottom of the problem.

Armed with the trusty hoe, Homer soon discovered the source of the teeth marks on Dolly's southern exposure. Peering into the toilet hole, he came eyeball to eyeball with a crotchety old settin' hen all fluffed out on her nest. I think maybe that's where the old sayin', "Madder 'n a Wet Hen" got started.

"There's times when I'm glad we ain't got a cook out here, Billy.
'Magine gettin' all that fired up about a danged ol' chicken."

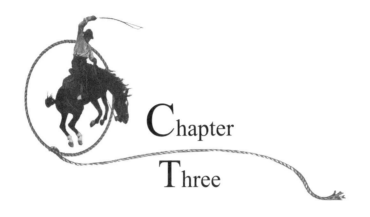

Chapter Three

The Longhorn~ Harley Davidson Cross

*T*he sun was just beginning to peak over the ridge, breakfast was in full swing, and Dick and Billy were having the same conversation they'd had ever' morning for about six months.

"How 'bout a hotcake?" Dick asked his old partner as he flips a couple on his own plate.

"Nope," was Billy's slurred reply as he popped the top on another beer. "I'm shtickin' with the Breakfast of Champions."

The two old bachelor cronies had been sort of on the outs the last few months. Dick had quit drinkin' last fall sometime and wanted his ol' buddy to experience all of the joys of sobriety that he'd gotten so accustomed to. There were times when the conversations got a little tense.

"I'm tellin' ya Billy, that drinkin' is gonna kill you. Have a hotcake. You need somethin' decent in yer stomach. That big red nose of yours looks just like a doorknob on the Fire Hall."

"Nuthin' worse than a reformed drunk," Billy retorted, his bleary eyes filled with inebriated contempt. "Eat them things yerself. Door knob on a Fire Hall, my foot! I feel sorry fer you, Dick. You got nuthin' to look forward to. When you wake up in the mornin' that's as good as you're gonna feel all day long. Me... now I know I'm gonna feel better than this after while."

The conversations always just seemed to trail off into the sunset with neither side of the argument getting the upper hand. They were both a little on the stubborn side and neither one of 'em would give an inch.... besides, they'd been partners far too long to get real mad at each other.

"We better get goin' if we're gonna make that circle before the sun gets too high," Billy changed the subject. He flipped the now empty beer can into the old thirty gallon oil drum by the door as he went out.

"Yea.... we better," Dick answered as he tidied up the table. "Give ol' Roany a feed of oats for me, will you? I'll be right behind you."

The boys struck out in a long trot for the west end of their summer pasture to look things over. They'd had a shower or two, the grass was good, and it was a perfect mornin' for a ride. Just as they topped the ridge on the south end of the field, they spied one of the neighbor's cows in with theirs. She was a big dry red brindle cow with a set of horns that belonged in the movies.

"Looks like we've got one of Smokey's cows in here again."

Normally they would have just eased her over to a gate and put her back where she belonged, but those horns were just more of a temptation than a trigger happy cowboy could stand. The critter looked like she must have been a Longhorn/Limousine cross, for she weighed in at around fourteen hundred pounds.

24

"Just look at those antlers," Dick grinned as he jerked down his rope. "I've got the head." Down the coulee towards their unsuspecting victim the two tumbleweed cowboys galloped.

The ol' girl threw her head up and put her tail over her back the minute she saw them comin', and took off on a high lope for the hole in the fence she'd crawled through. She didn't quite make it, and let out a beller that would raise the dead when the slack came out of the loop that Dick had neatly placed around her horns.

Billy's end wasn't quite as easy. The sagebrush was tall and thick so the healin' part of the operation was a little on the tricky side. A couple of loops later and he had her. The boys stretched the old cow out on the sagebrush flat on the far side of the ridge.

They were proud as punch of their little piece of cowboy fun, but to say that the bellerin' cow wasn't impressed would be an understatement.

"That ought to teach her to stay home," Dick grinned as he stepped off his horse and walked over to the cow stretched out on the ground to retrieve his rope from those huge horns. As he straddled her neck and pulled his loop loose, Billy rode up to loosen his rope on her hind feet.

This is an operation that the boys had performed at least a jillion times. It's just standard procedure for turnin' a critter loose. But this time Billy was a little quick on the draw and released the slack on his end just as Dick was astraddle the cow's neck. Up she came, with one of Dick's legs on each side and a hand on each of those giant horns.

They just thought the ol' cow was upset before. She took off like a rocket; bellerin' and hookin' at Dick with her antlers. They were almost perfect handlebars, and he really put up a dandy ride. It's a dang shame it wasn't captured on video.

25

Boy, what a sight. Dick's long legs were draggin' the ground on each side of her neck with the rowels on his big Mexican spurs whirrin' through the prairie grass, and cutting little trenches. Both hands were firmly gripped on those wonderful Longhorn-Harley Davidson handlebars.

About this time Billy's Border Collie couldn't stand not being in on the action, and ran around to the front and grabbed the already irate cow by the nose. She dropped her head to hook the dog and off went Dick, landing in a heap right in front of his former mode of transportation.

"Ah, there he is!" Ol Brindle thought to herself and made a hook at the seat of Dick's Wranglers. The horn slid right over the intended target and lodged itself firmly under his belt. This deal isn't getting any better from Dick's perspective. He's flat on his belly now with a mad cow's horn stuck in the back of his belt. She's as intent on getting loose from Dick as he is from her, but at the present time her focus is on the dog that's still taking every opportunity to nibble away at her face.

The powerful old cow is galloping across the prairie after the dog with a horn under Dick's belt and his face making a little furrow through the rocks and sagebrush.

Billy's thinkin' this is about the funniest thing he's ever seen, and would give his whole calf check for a camera.

The belt buckle finally broke, the cow ran off, and Dick managed to drag himself back to his feet. He was a real mess. His clothes were nearly torn off, and the ride through the sagebrush hadn't done his face any good.

"You really don't look THAT bad," Billy grinned, barely able to contain his laughter. ".... 'cept fer yer nose.... looks like a door knob on the Fire Hall."

"I think thatus about the funniest thing I ever'
saw, Dick. If 'n you'd o' had a decent breakfast
in ya like me you mighta even o' got 'er rode."

Chapter Four

The Horse Tradin'-Bull Shippin' Grandma

*T*here are a couple of guidelines that a fella can pretty well count on. They're not cut in stone, mind you.... but they do seem to hold true, at least most of the time. The first one concerns horse traders and their famous propensity to exaggerate some of the facts, forget to tell you a few of the others, and just plain bald faced lie when the need arises. I know this really isn't news to any of you with a little experience with one of these guys. In fact, it's a practice that's considered almost normal.... sort of like a genetic defect. The guy just CAN'T tell the whole truth, and most folks just have that figured out goin' into the deal.

The other principle that you can nearly always hang your hat on is that nice mild mannered Christian Grandmas are usually on the level. They tend to spend a lot of their time in the Good Book studying up for their final exams, and the result of all that Bible readin' just sort of naturally bubbles out in fairly decent behavior. The ones I know would die before they told you a whopper.

This all leads me to a little story a friend of mine related to me last week. Now, I'm goin' to tell this just the way it was told to me, and you'll have to make up your own mind whether to believe it or not. Somehow I've gotten sort of a bad reputation for jumblin' up the facts on occasion. I can't figure out how that ever happened, but I swear that this deal is exactly the way I heard it.

> **"...and Bible readin' Grandmas are usually on the level."**

The problem with the believin' part of this story is that it really DOES sound sort of far-fetched, and the source is both a horse trader AND a Christian Grandma. So, now what do you do? Helen Beeson is not only the Head and Horns of the Terry Ranch down by Virgelle, but she falls right smack dab in the middle of both of the above categories. You'll have to make up your own mind.

Here she goes. It was a nice warm late summer evening, and Helen was sitting in her rockin' chair with her trusty cane and Good Book by her side. She was just minding her own business; waiting for the riders to get back from up the coulee with the bulls they were gatherin'.

Being a little warm like it was, a couple of the old boys got on the fight, so the cowboys left one of the bulls in the brush, and then headed the other one towards the headquarters. Down the coulee he came at a high lope. He really had blood in his eye and Duchess, the Border Collie, that kept nippin'... heels-nose-heels all the way home didn't help his disposition a bit.

30

After they finally got him lined out, the dog did most of the work, but by the time the bull got down by the ranch house, his patience was wearin' a little thin. Little Duchess ran around the front again, just like those Borders love to do, and gave Mr. Ferdinand another little love nip on his upper lip.

That was the last straw! The bull dropped his head and lit into Duchess with a vengeance. She was too quick for him, though and ducked around the corner of the house and up on the porch. Ferdinand lost sight of his target, but there tied on a chain just mindin' his own business was Coalie, Helen's Blue Healer/Ausie cross watch dog. She had him tied up because, as ever'body knows, too many stock dogs can sometimes mess up the soup. The bull closed in for the kill, and Coalie lit out for parts unknown.

"Hey, I'm innocent!" he was probably yellin' over his shoulder. You got the wrong guy! Duchess is the one you're after!"

A dog is a dog if you're an upset bull, and this old boy was plenty hot. He was lookin' for a canine critter to iron out flat, and this one will do just fine. Coalie acted like a complete coward.... until he hit the end of the 20 foot chain, but then most ever'body will put up a fight when he's cornered, and when the chain jerked him back around to face his pursuer, Coalie was loaded for bear. He also took a nice big chomp out of Ferdie's face causing the bull to wheel back around facing the house.

"Oh no!" The poor old bull must have been thinkin'. "There's a couple more of the varmints!" There right in his line of sight with their feet up on the inside of the glass porch door were Helen's two little house dogs, Furbie and Shivers. Neither one of them are as big as a pound of soap, but boy can they ever yap. They were brave as they could be, being safe inside like they were, and were raisin' an awful ruckus.

The bull dropped his head and charged his two new enemies. He hit the glass door once, and the little guys in the house yapped even louder. Right about now it's entirely possible that Duchess and Coalie got back into the game, and each got a hold of a hind leg. There aren't any actual witnesses to this part, and whether the bull got any extra encouragement from the rear or not sure didn't change the results. He hit the glass door the second time, and this time he came right on in.... with those two little lap dogs zeroed in his sights.

Hellen Beeson & Chipper

Now, Helen has never been accused of bein' a quitter. She's been known to hold her own with many an ornery critter, but she took one look at that cane in her hand (her only means of defense), then took a gander at that snot slingin' bull with blood in his eye, and it only took about three/fifths of a second to calculate the odds. There are times when a hasty retreat is the better part of valor, so she didn't waste any time ducking into the nearest bedroom and closing the door.

Furbie and Shivers didn't feel nearly so brave and tough when their opponent was face to face with them in the living room, so they made a beeline for their little screened in cage. The bull took a hook at the couch and the clothes layin' on the back of it on the way by, and wound up with a sweatshirt over his face that covered up both his eyes.

That was just the lucky break that the two little pooches needed, as Ferdinand completely lost sight of where they went. The second lucky break came when the bull slung his head again, throwing off his blindfold. By chance it landed right on the dog cage and being in the dark and scared enough to wet themselves, the two little dogs completely quit their barkin'.

Unable to locate his target, and feeling a little boxed in, the old bull made another circle or two through the living room, hooking Helen's purse and throwing it into the kitchen and then made his escape out the same hole he'd entered.

It sure could have been a whole lot worse. The dogs could've run down the hall, and if the bull had gone that way, it's quite possible he'd have torn the whole house down before he got back out. A bull can raise cane with a corral just turning around in an alleyway, much less trying that trick in the hallway of your house.

They say all's well that ends well, but if Helen had been a little slower getting that bedroom door shut, you just might be reading this on the Obituary Page. Now, I told you this was quite a story, and Helen swears it's true. She has several witnesses, too.... but I'll be doggoned..... ever' one of 'em is a horsetrader.

"There ain't no fool like an old fool
You've heard that often said.
I just hope I get to be one
'Afore they find me dead."

Chapter Five

Really Starvin'

There were three guys that did a lot of travelin' on the amateur rodeo circuit back in the fifties, and a stranger would have thought they hated each other the way they carried on. Those boys, like a lot of the other "knights of the plains" that I've known, had a real twisted sense of humor, and as a result, were often misunderstood by those outside their crudely warped social circle. (Not that they really gave a hoot.) Although I don't think they would ever actually inflict real pain on one of their own kind intentionally, they seemed to almost enjoy seeing something bad happen to one of their compadres.

One of the guys was named Bob Biddy. He came from down in the Black Hills someplace and was a real bronc stompin' fool. He was a little guy, not much over five feet tall, and barely weighed a hundred pounds, so he naturally got the nickname, "Itty". (Itty Biddy does have sort of a ring to it, doesn't it?) He sure could ride. He and Nolan Parker and Johnny (alias "Squeaky") Ellis were about as thick as thieves. Nolan was a pretty good-sized guy from Wyoming, and Johnny was a Canadian with a squeaky little voice. He sounded like a set of rusty hinges on a barn door ever' time he said something. They were all good hands, and what they wouldn't pull on each other isn't worth mentioning. It seemed like the sky was the limit.

Unfortunately, they could all see the end of their free livin' "Three Musketeers" life. Romance got the best of Itty. He got all tangled up with a long legged blonde barrel racer from over in the western part of the state, and they set a date. I believe her name was Marcie, and the weddin' bells were about to ring. Deep inside, I think Nolan and Squeeky were a little jealous. The bride was a real dish, and although she was about six or eight inches taller than Itty, it didn't seem to bother either one of them very much. These two so-called friends of the groom hatched a plan to pull a good one on their poor ol' travelin' partner.

It was a big church weddin' and the boys were perfect gentlemen right through the whole deal. Itty was afraid they would get to drinkin' and embarrass him in front of his new bride's family, but he was pleasantly surprised. They were all cleaned up and didn't have a sniff of anything to drink. They even kept a lid on their barnyard vocabulary. Little did the hapless groom know that their wicked plans would soon begin to unfold.

In the midst of the reception just before the cake cutting ceremony, someone distracted the groom long enough that Nolan and Johnny stole the bride, and out the door they went. Now, stealin' the bride on her wedding day really isn't an original trick in these parts, but these two jokers took it to a whole new level. They had already purchased three roundtrip tickets on the Empire Builder to Saint Paul, and away they went. (This was back in the pre-Amtrak days, when the trains still ran on time)

Marcie thought it was a big joke until the train actually pulled out of the station. The boys tried to tease her out of it, but when she found out they were headed for Saint Paul, she cried for at least two hours, and then got "madder 'n a wet hen", and stayed that way for a couple of hundred miles. Itty thought it was funny for the first few minutes, but it wasn't long until he was fit to be tied. He couldn't find his sweetie anyplace, and would have gladly shot the two clowns on the spot if he'd had any idea where to find 'em. They must have been quite a sight. It's not too often you see a bride in her long white weddin' gown on a three day vacation…. without the groom.

Three days later they got back to town, and decided to drop Itty's bride off in front of his house and then take off before the lead started flyin'.

"We'll just leave you right here by the door," Squeaky offered congenially. "We wouldn't want you to miss the rest of yer honeymoon."

"Thanks!" Marcie snapped. "I'll get you Johnny Ellis…. you just wait. That goes for you too Parker," she snarled at Nolan as she slammed the pickup door. Itty was just coming out of the house as they threw the pickup in gear and headed down the road.

Mr. and Mrs. Biddy got over it. After a month or two the friendship was as good as new. It's funny how things work, though. About a year later, Nolan had found himself a little honey that had gotten him all haltered up and headed for the alter. He was worried stiff about the upcoming wedding. His vivid memory was brimmin' with all the dirty tricks he'd pulled in the past, and paybacks can be a real bummer.

His two old pals were at the wedding. Marcie had Itty pretty well house broke by this time, and Squeaky was on his best behavior. Nolan didn't get more than a foot away from his new bride all during the reception. He **KNEW** he couldn't trust those two outlaws he occasionally called friends. His feelings were almost hurt. They didn't try a thing.

The new couple left the uneventful reception and stole away to a secret little bungalow they had reserved for their honeymoon. It was nearly a hundred miles down the road, and Nolan kept a sharp eye out, making sure they weren't being followed. They'd made it. Their's was the only outfit on the road.

Nolan carried his new bride over the threshold of their honeymoon cottage and into an evening of marital bliss. They spent their enchanted wedding night, enthralled in each other's charms, and awoke just as the sun was beginning to peak through the east window.

"What do you say? Should we go get some breakfast?" Nolan cooed to his bride. "Are you hungry?" It was then that his worst fears were realized. From under the bed came Squeaky's unmistakable voice.

"Good idea! I'm starvin'! How 'bout you Itty?"

"Yea, me too!"

Such is life in the far, far, West.

"Now that's disgusting. I'm sure glad that didn't happen on one of my honeymoons."

38

Chapter Six

The Unflappable Brother Van

*I*t's hard to imagine I know, but I've actually been accused of stretching the truth. One guy even called me a "bald-faced liar". Now I really think that may be a little strong, don't you? Although I've never let a little thing like the facts get in the way of tellin' a good story, I really would rather refer to any inconstancies as "creative truth enhancement". But now if this little tale isn't all the truth, then it ain't my fault, because with my hand on a stack of Bibles, I'll swear it's just like I heard it. Embellishment just isn't necessary.

One of the foremost circuit ridin' preachers of the early days of Montana was Brother Van. Actually his real name was William Wesley Van Orsdel. That seemed far too long and dignified to the patrons of the Four Deuces Saloon in Fort Benton, so he was dubbed "Brother Van". It was to this motley crew of trappers, cowboys, gamblers, and dance hall girls that he preached his very first sermon in Montana Territory.

The story goes that he got off the Missouri River steamboat and headed for the first establishment he could see on Main Street to enquire about a place where he could hold a church service. Much to his surprise, the bartender banged the handle of his six-shooter on the bar and ordered everyone to shut up and listen. The crowd quieted, the card games stopped, and Brother Van mounted a chair and began to sing an old gospel song. He soon had the crowd enthralled, and his reputation as a man of God who wasn't afraid to associate with the folks he was trying to reach with the Good News was born.

William Wesley Van Orsdel
"Brother Van"

He started untold numbers of Methodist Churches in the Territory, and the one in our little hometown of Chinook is no exception. He chose the highest knob in the settlement, which was the custom in the old days. I suppose the logic was that if a church occupied the high point in town with the steeple rising towards heaven, the building would have a symbolic as well as a spiritual presence. It must have worked at least in this instance, because even though the highest piece of real estate in our town just happened to be across the street from the brothel, the old church is still flourishing and the house of ill fame is long since gone.

A few years ago, I played some music in the old church Brother Van built in Bannack back in the 1870's. Bannack was the Territorial Capital of Montana in the old mining days, and the young preacher just happened to be in town when the "Battle of the Big Hole" took place. It's just over the hill a few miles to the battlefield site where Chief Joseph's Nez Pierce band had a run in with the US Cavalry. The frightened settlers flocked into town from the outlying areas fearing an Indian attack, and braced and barricaded the little settlement against the assault that never came.

It's funny how the fear of impending death can affect the spiritual attitudes of some of the most reprobate of characters, and the resourceful Brother Van seized the opportunity to not only preach the Message of Grace but to also mobilize his degenerate flock into the construction of a church building that stands to this day.

Everyone seemed to like this kindly Eastern man of the cloth. Charlie Russell painted a picture of Brother Van hunting buffalo with the Blackfeet. The painting depicts the preacher and his horse, racing along side his Indian companions through the sea of stampeding animals with his long black coat tails streaming in the wind, and his old Navy Colt blazing away. He was a friend to all.

On another occasion, he was riding in a stagecoach that was held up by a band of robbers. With shotguns and pistols drawn, the highwaymen forced the coach to a halt and ordered the driver and the passengers to unload.

"Get out of the coach, and keep your hands in the air."

The frightened passengers carefully climbed out of the stagecoach, trying not to unduly provoke the desperate bandits. They knew all too well that many of the foiled robberies in that area had resulted in murders. Under the watchful eye of the leader, his double-barreled shotgun leveled at the victims, one of the gang members began to collect their money and the valuables. One by one the passengers eagerly forfeited everything in their possession.

But when the young robber approached Brother Van, he got a different response. The man of God looked straight into the highwayman's eyes and asked, "You wouldn't rob a poor old Methodist minister, would you?"

The question seemed to take the outlaw by surprise, as he stopped short and thought a second or two before replying, "@#*% no I won't.... after all.... I'm a &%$# Methodist too!"

Chapter Seven

Go Goat Go

Do you remember that old nursery rhyme about Jack Sprat? It goes like this:

Jack Sprat could eat no fat
His wife could eat no lean
So betwixt the two of them
They licked the platter clean

In the book I had as a kid, there was a picture of this skinny little man standing beside an absolutely huge woman, and every time I see Bob and Carol, I think about that little rhyme.

I've always wondered how in the dickens they can even sleep together. Carol's weight would make ever' place else on the bed uphill from there. Poor ol' Bob must have to keep one leg hooked over the side just to keep from rolling to the middle and windin' up underneath that massive mound of womanhood. It looks just plain dangerous to me.

I guess they must have figured out how to manage a few of those little details through the years, because they seem to get along famously, and they've done pretty well in the ranchin' business, too. Bob is a real cowboy, and as such, really hasn't got much time for what he calls "Ma's silliness". Carol's pet goats are one of the things that fall into that category, and so when it comes to them, she's on her own. He figures he's just too busy makin' a livin' to mess with them.

One day a month or so ago, Carol was in town gettin' her hair fixed and as soon as she drove back into the yard she could see that Flossy was sick.... real sick.

"Bobby!" she hollered across the yard, "Come quick! There's something wrong with Flossy!" Bob was just loading his horse in the trailer, and had the pickup loaded up with fencin' material, but he dutifully trudged across the yard.... he knew there'd be hell to pay if he didn't at least take a look. There was poor ol' Flossy. Her head was hangin' down, her long ears were flopped down over her eyes, and there was a big hump in her back.

"Yup, she's sick alright. Don't take no rocket scientist to see that," was Bob's compassionate observation.

"What's the matter? What should I do?" Carol pleaded. It wasn't too hard to see the problem. Between Flossy's front feet was what remained of a stick of belt dressing Bob had used on one of the v belts on the swather, and the sticky fuzz on her bottom lip revealed where the rest of it had gone.... down Flossy's throat.

"Them **&%$#** goats will eat anything. The **%$#&** thing's plugged up. Better give her some mineral oil to loosen her back up. I'm goin' ridin'. The yearlin's are out up north." With that, Bob turned on his heal, and headed to work, leaving Carol to deal with Flossy.

Carol hurried to change her clothes and then got a hose and ran a quart or so of mineral oil down her baby's throat.

The only thing to do now was to wait. The belt dressing had done its dastardly deed, and Flossy's insides were stuck solid. The waiting was hard, the time just seemed to drag by, and the goat seemed to be getting worse, not better. After a couple of hours, Carol couldn't wait any longer. She called the Vet, who advised her to bring Flossy right in.

There was only one little problem. Her little Bobby had taken the pickup and trailer, and she had no way to get her baby to town except in the backseat of her new Lincoln. Country girls learn young that "You gotta do what you gotta do", so an old blanket was quickly spread across the backseat, and Carol gently laid Flossy on it and headed for town.

"Just hang on baby. The Doctor will make you all better," Carol consoled as they pulled out of the yard.

The first part of the trip was completely uneventful. They had about twenty miles of gravel road before they got to the pavement, and other than a few mornful groans, Flossy seemed to 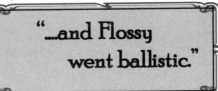 be in her own little world, too miserable to even notice she was on the way to town. Unfortunately, there is a railroad crossing just before the turn onto the highway, and as luck would have it, there was the old Westbound 88 whistlin' loudly towards the crossing.

Flossy went ballistic. She started running around in circles in the backseat, and making scared little goat sounds, tangling the blanket into a wad with her feet as she went. It fell on the floor, spookin' the goat even more, and leaving the new seat cushion exposed to her sharp little feet. Reassurances from Carol in the front of the car didn't seem to have any effect whatsoever. The poor little thing had never seen or heard a train before, and was scared plumb to death. She started banging her head into the side windows in a desperate attempt at escape.

That's when Carol got her brainy idea. She hit the control button for the window on the passenger side of the back, and rolled it down about six inches. On the next circle, just as Flossy stuck her head out the hole, Carol hit the up button. It was a brilliant plan…. the kind that makes you proud you thought of it. Oh, she didn't roll it up enough to hurt her baby…. just enough to hold her head, and keep her from running in circles.

"…. and Flossy came unplugged."

Here is where the plan takes a little turn to the south. Flossy really went berserk now. Her head was stuck, the train was whistlin', and unless she could get loose, she was certain she was gonna die. She began to pull back as hard as she could in a frantic attempt to free herself from the monster that had grabbed her.

46

All of her pulling and bleating and straining were to no avail. There was just no way to pull herself loose. The only thing to move was the plug in Flossy's bowels. A big wad of belt dressing about the size of a tennis ball hit Carol's new hair-do right behind her right ear. That was followed immediately by the mineral oil, and everything else Flossy had eaten in the last twenty-four hours.

Carol decided that a trip to the Vet wasn't as urgent as it was a little earlier, so she just went shoppin' for a new car instead.

"Doggone it, Billy. Whenever I get t' feeling' sorry fer myself about not havin' me a cook like Bobby's got, I figger I'm jus' like this ol' dog o' ours.... Lucky"

Chapter Eight

The Eye Patch Story

*B*eing a one-eyed singin' cowboy really has its ups and downs. One of the good deals is that I'm a real hit with the girls. Unfortunately that's also one of the bad parts.... for some reason it seems that all the ladies I impress are either over eighty or under ten. I'm really glad that those two categories think I'm wonderful, but that leaves about seventy years worth of girls that could care less, and that sort of concerns me. If my dream to become a cowboy sex symbol is ever going to come to fruition, I think maybe I need to tune my act up a little.

I sure get a lot of questions about this durn eye patch. A few folks have even wondered if it was just a part of my act. My modest reply is always the same; "Do you actually think that a guy with a face this purty would cover half of it up for no reason at all?" Actually it's because I can't see out of the eye it covers up anyway. If I look straight south of here towards Billings, the right one sort of goes over towards Spokane someplace. When I don't wear the patch, and happen to wave at someone in a crowd, half the place is liable to wave back.... nobody's really too sure who I'm lookin' at. My Ma always says, "I never borned you that way.", and 'course she's right. It was just a dumb accident that happened a long time ago.

Here's what happened: The cook and I had been married for three or four years and were living up on Clear Creek, working for Harry Olson. I usually always had a colt that needed riding, so after supper ever' evening, I'd saddle up and take a ride. The trail from the barn to the pasture went right past the house, and every night I'd see my little bride standing in the window as I rode past. Of course, she was proud as punch of her cowboy and I got this wonderful idea one day to make a few extra points with her. I tried it out that very night. I've figured out (through many years of bad experience) that if you just toss the reins at most colts to give him their head and stick a little spur in their belly, that the majority of them will bog their head and buck a little.

There are three things here I need to point out about most young cowboys:

1. Any cowboy worth his salt has an itchy ropin' arm. (This doesn't have anything to do with the story... it's just the truth.)

2. They're always trying to prove how well they can ride, so encouraging a colt to buck is not entirely out of their character.

3. They're **ALL** trying to figure out how to impress girls. It was the last two of these that helped me lose my eye. It seems I was always trying to ride some boneheaded bronc, and after all these years, I'm still trying my best to impress that same gal.

The secret was to get the colt to buck right in front of the window, without the little woman figuring out that I was doing it on purpose. A good spur jab right in the cinch on the side she couldn't see, along with givin' him his head, did the job ever' time. I'd ride and fan my hat, and she'd swoon..... what a guy won't go through to gain a little feminine favor.

The problem was that the colt was learnin' how to buck faster than I was learnin' how to ride, and the last night I tried it, he almost ironed me out. Now, that would have been a real catastrophe. I always ride colts with an old Joseph Sullivan saddle that was made in Fort Benton back in the 1890's. It's one of those old high backed, wide forked, short-seated jobs that's pretty hard to fall out of. As a matter of fact, the only way out of that old thing is straight up. Bear trap saddle or not, I durn near got bucked off, and stood the chance of losing all the girl-impressin' points I'd managed to build up in the last couple of weeks.

The only thing to do was to shorten the stirrups up a little, and then **TRY** to keep him from buckin' again. I don't imagine those old stirrup leathers been changed for fifty years or so, and the old laces were pretty hard and stiff. Oh, I got the dang things unlaced all right, but couldn't get them to go back into the other holes. So with the leathers between my knees, I decide to pull on the itty-bitty end of the lace with a pair of needle nosed pliers. It really wasn't a very good idea. They slipped off, and I stuck the pliers in my eye. To make things even worse, it was Christmas Eve.

I think maybe it was guys that operate the way I do that made the Good Lord decide to give us two eyes in the first place.... but then my wife says I see way more than I'm supposed to with the one I've got left.

Wonderful Stuff

It 'll fix a rusty bicycle chain
Or quiet a squeekin' door
Or you can rub it on your chappin' lips
But hold on Pardner there's more

My favorite use for Vaseline
Is when I'm lovin' on my heart throb....
I jus' rub it all over the door handle, Son
So's the kids can't turn the knob.

Chapter Nine

The Loosh Moosh

The sun was just peekin' over the ridge as Dick and Billy finished loading their horses in the trailer. They had to go to Billings to drop Red Busby off at one of those spin dry boardin' houses for drunks. Red had been hittin' the bottle way too hard, even by their standards, and someone needed to take control of the situation before he drank himself to death. As long as they were going to town anyway, they figured to take in a ropin' while they were there…. no sense wastin' a trip.

"Wonder how ol' Red's gonna take us dumpin' him off down there?" Billy was thinking out loud as they eased their outfit out of the yard. Red just lives four or five miles down the road to the east of their place.

"He ain't even gonna know the difference for a while. We'll probably have to carry him to the pickup anyway. The hard part is gonna be talkin' him in to signin' himself in at the hospital when we finally get there."

Red was in about the shape they'd expected... or maybe even a little worse. There was no way he could make it to the pickup on his own power, but the boys got him poured into the cab and were on the road in fairly short order.

"Here, have a cup o' coffee Red," Billy offered, pouring a cup from the big Thermos they'd brought along. Red grudgingly obliged, knowing that the boys were probably up to something. He never did like wreckin' a good drunk with coffee. The plan was to sober him up on the five hour trip to Billings and then to somehow convince him that takin' the cure for his obvious booze problem was a good idea.

It was nearly noon by the time they found the treatment center. Now the trick was to find a place to park the pickup and trailer that was close enough that Red could walk.... he still wasn't motorin' all that well. They finally gave up. Dick and Red got out by the front door of the hospital, and Billy drove on to find a place to park. He located a great spot in the shade on a side street, but it was about four blocks away from where he'd dropped his partners off.

"Dang good thing we didn't try to make that red-headed old bugger walk this far," Billy muttered to himself. "He'd o' never made it."

Of course, because it was the noon hour there wasn't anyone to check them in, so they camped out on a bench by the front door of the hospital. It was a nice cool shady spot, and it felt good to give their legs a good stretch after the long trip. Dick had already broken the news to Red by the time Billy returned, and they were sure hoping that he'd sign the papers without a fuss. They had no choice but to wait for the hospital folks to come back from dinner, so they spent it givin' the ol' boy a real sales pitch.

"Booyss I jushed think yer makin' a big deal out o' nuthin'," Red slobbered. "A lil drink now an' again never hurt nobody."

54

"Now this is fer yer own good, Red," Dick replied. "Yer liver ain't gonna take this forever, ya know."

Just then the lady that manned the front desk whisked past and unlocked the front door, and the boys followed her right in, explaining the whole way why they were there. As expected, the receptionist reminded them that Red would have to sign the entrance papers.

"Sure he'll sign 'em. Won't cha, Red?" Billy replied, shoving a pen in Red's shaky paw. Red didn't answer, as Billy guided his trembling hand to the right line on the paper. "Just put yer John Henry right there, Red."

Red slobberd something under his kerosene breath and proceeded to scrawl a few scribbley lines on the paper. The receptionist put on her glasses and gazed at the ink squiggle on the entrance form for a few seconds before asking, "What did you say your name was, Sir?"

"It's Red Busby, Ma'am," Billy quipped as he pointed to the inky scrawl. "Can't you make that out?"

"No sir! I can't, and if you can I'm certain we can find a room here for you! Please take Mr. Busby outside and work on his sobriety for another hour or two. This is totally unacceptable. He has to be able to write legibly before admittance is possible."

The boys were a little down in the mouth as they guided Red back out to the park bench, and poured him another cup of coffee. Red's eyes looked like two burnt holes in a sheepskin. He gazed off into space up the street for a few seconds and then casually inquired, "Either one of you boyz got any ushe fer a three 'er four year ol' moosh?"

"Dad Blame it, Red! That's why we got you down here. Yer plumb out of yer head," Dick yelled in exasperation, his patience nearly at its end. "You see the dangdest stuff!"

"Well, I'll tell you somethin'…. I ain't had a drink all mornin'," Billy interrupted as he followed Red's bleary gaze. "But I think he's right! That dang shore looks like a moose to me!"

55

Sure enough there she was. A cow moose trottin' up the street in Billings, Montana, right in the middle of the day. "You stay here with Red and keep yer eye on that moose," Billy hollered over his shoulder. "I'm goin' after my horse." He lit a shuck for the trailer, and the poor old confused moose sort of stopped and took a couple of bites off of a nearby hedge, and then turned and trotted up a side street.

A couple of minutes later the clickity-click of horse-shoes could be heard on the asphalt street as Billy came

on a dead run, jerkin' his rope down as he came. "She went up that way," Dick pointed.

"Never sheen nobody rope a moosh before," Red slobbered. Billy rounded the corner with his rope in hand and headed in the direction of his intended target. There weren't any witnesses to the actual ropin' part of this story, as it took place a couple of streets over from Dick and Red, but there isn't much doubt as to what really happened. Billy caught her all right, and claims that it wasn't all that hard. The problem arose when he took his dallies and tried to slow her down.

"Shounds like he's killin' 'er," Red drawled as the awfulest beller you ever heard came from the direction of the clickity-click of the horseshoes.

Apparently Ms. Moose wasn't hurt a bit, because she turned and came back up the slack of that rope with a cowboy and his bay geldin' in her sights. Billy came back around the corner even faster than he'd gone around it the first time, closely followed by a deranged female moose with blood in her eye. The loop end of his rope was neatly placed around her neck right behind her ears, and Billy and the Bay were desperately trying to keep as much of the slack out of the rest of it as possible.

The last time they saw them, Billy was headed down the street towards the Bear Tooth Mountains as hard as he could go with a bellerin' moose hot on his tail.

"Well, now I sheen somebody rope a moosh," Red slobbered philosophically. "Shure would like to see someone try to turn one loosh."

"Yea, I did sort of have a tough time gettin' my rope back, Dick. But you'd o' never even caught 'er on that ol' plug you was ridin."

Chapter Ten

Calling All Eunuchs

$\mathcal{W}$e just got Kody Gilge married off a couple of weeks ago. I sure hope his poor little bride knows what she was getting herself into. I've told a few stories on Kody through the years, all of them the truth, I might add. A fella could write a book on all the things that little buzzard did when he was a sprout.

He was a neighbor kid that just wouldn't go away.... sort of like pig manure on your boots. Wherever you went there he was, asking his endless stream of questions, and offering unwanted advice on everything from tractor mechanics to world politics. Kody just isn't "normal".... what ever normal is, and at the risk of him hitting me up for royalties (again), I need to tell you a couple more little tales.

It was the spring of the year, and I was working up some ground over by his house. I knew it was just a matter of time until the little rascal showed up. Sure enough, I hadn't been in the field over a half an hour until across the freshly turned earth he ran. If you can just visualize a combination of the little guy they called Pigpen in the Charlie Brown comic strip and Dennis the Menace, you have a pretty good idea of how the little character looked and acted. His Mom could have him all shined up with clean clothes on, and in 10 minutes he'd look like he just climbed out of a dumpster.

"Hey! You need some help?"

"Sure, Kody," I answered stopping the tractor and helping him up on the fender. Getting along without his "help" was pretty much unavoidable.

Kody Gilge
The Original Lil' Rascal

Although I can't remember any of it, I'm sure our conversation was varied and lively. There might even have been enough time for me to squeeze a word in once in a while if I talked fast enough.

Heaven only knows where they come from, but the seagulls show up around here the minute you turn over some fresh ground. We never see them any other time, but just start farmin' and in fifteen minutes they're all over the place. This morning was no exception, and they showed up by the hundreds.

Of course with Spring in full bloom, the gentlemen seagulls were showing a lot of interest in the lady seagulls, and many of them were fairly demonstrative in their displays of affection. It sure didn't take my little "helper" long to take note of that either.

"Hey!" he yelled pointing a dirty little finger, "What's goin' on over there?"

"Oh, I don't know," I answered casually, looking the other way. "They must be fightin' or something." It's an answer that really should have worked, after all the kid was only five years old. But then he isn't "normal", remember?

"Well maybe," he quipped, "but it looks like they're mating to me."

How in the world do you deal with a kid like that?

"I don't know, maybe that is what they're doin'. I don't know anything about seagulls. Maybe you better ask your Dad." Nuthin' like passin' the buck.

His continuous streams of probing questions were a real pain in the neck, and a lot of the time they were just plain embarrassin' for the questionee. Then there were those other times when he'd ask a completely naive childlike question, and his Dad who is deaf as a post in one ear, wouldn't quite catch the drift.

"Dad, what's a unit?" Kody asked one day in his innocence.

"A eunuch?" his hard of hearing Father repeated, hoping that he'd misunderstood the question while his mind desperately searched for an adequate (truthful, but not TOO truthful) answer.

"Yea."

"This kid is only five years old," thought Dad to himself, "he doesn't need to know this stuff." But, not wanting to lie to him, he launched into a Biblical explanation that talked all around the question but really didn't confront it head on.

I've run into a lot of folks a whole lot older than Kody that didn't know what a eunuch was either, so in case you're one of them, I'll give you the PG rated, Reader's Digest answer. They were the steer-ified male slaves owned by the kings back in biblical times, that were charged with the responsibility for the care and protection of the King's harem. (Explain that one to a five-year-old.)

Boy, would the ACLU have a heyday with that one. But then, on the other hand, when a fella was faced with some of the alternatives, maybe it wasn't as bad as it sounds.

From a modern human rights perspective the practice seems pretty well out in left field, but back in the days when both slaves and women were considered property, it was fairly common and considered a sound business practice. By all the accounts I've read, it was pretty effective, too. What a nice tidy way of protecting the king's personal assets from any outside threats, while at the same time protecting the king's assets from the guy that was protecting the king's assets. Makes sense to me.

Dad's ears were probably turning a little red as he stammered around; doing everything he could to answer the little guy's question without really telling him anything. After about ten minutes of stumbling around and stepping on his tongue, he was finally done. He looked at the puzzled expression on the little shaver's face, and looking him straight in his big brown eyes asked, "Any more questions?"

I doubt if Dad was really prepared for the response he got. After ten minutes of tortured explanation, Kody wasn't any closer to an answer than when they'd begun.

"Yea.... I still don't understand.... why on all the cop shows on TV are they always "Calling all Units."

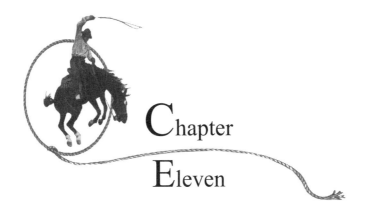

Chapter Eleven

Dolly The Calf Thief

*D*olly and I had a love/hate relationship. It was sort of like bein' married to a big raw boned woman that got a lot of the ranch work done, but gave you a black eye ever so often. She'd be dang shore hard to get along with, but she WAS really handy around the outfit, and because you weren't real sure you could whup her in a fair fight, you just make the best of it.

Ol' Dolly was a milk cow that we got from Otto Newman back in the early 70's. She looked like she was all Holstein, but she was supposed to have had a little Brown Swiss way back in her pedigree someplace, too. Those legs of hers were about as long as I've ever seen. She could almost clean the leftover hay out of the four wheel drive feedin' pickup by just walking around it and reaching over. All she would miss was just a little bit right in the middle behind the cab. No worries.... the old girl would just jump up in the back to finish off her lunch. What ever breed she was, she'd rank right up there in the top 10 money makers on this outfit, that's for sure.

The only reason she didn't talk, was because she didn't want to. That durn cow was smarter than most people (and ALL of the politicians.) We milked her quite a bit, and put extra calves on her for years. She'd claim any calf you put in the pen with her, and if she felt lonesome, she'd just go steal one from some other cow. That can be a real pain in the neck, and used to bug the heck out of me until I finally figured out how to use it to our advantage.

Come Spring of the year when all the neighbors got to calvin' good, I'd lock her calves away from her and turn her out on the County Road. She'd be standin' back by the barn waitin' for her grain by evening with a nice calf taggin' along by her side. She was usually good for three or four extra calves every spring. The good part was that the coyotes always got the blame for draggin' the calves off, and the ol' girl claimed them so well that the best Brand Inspector in the country would swear up and down that it was hers. Profits around here really hit the tank when she left.

There wasn't a gate or door on the place she couldn't open, either. She was forever getting into the grain bin, and boy what a catastrophe. Oh, it didn't hurt her any.... she was used to quite a feed of grain twice a day, but the other cows that followed her in there weren't, and we had sick cows to doctor more than once because of that old bag's tricks.

We tried to time her calvin' out so that she'd be fresh in the Spring when extra calves were plentiful. One year she'd had two or three on her and it was about the middle of June. The calves that were suckin' her were big enough to wean, and it was time to find her some more. The neighbors were all done calvin' so I had to go the Sale Barn to buy a couple. Boy, I hated to do that.... it really cuts into the profit, but that's what we did and then cut the big calves safely away from her (we thought), and locked them up in a different pen.

Right after dinner as I headed back out to work, I spied this little problem. Here's Dolly.... her hind leg all hiked back and her bag stuck over close to the fence so that one of the 400 pound lunkers we had just weaned off of her, could suck through the fence. I was hoppin' mad, let out a yell and reached down to pick up a rock. She saw me coming, and understanding my expletives perfectly, took off in a trot, jerking her calf's breakfast dispenser right out of his mouth. There he stood, his head stuck through the barbed wire fence, with milk slobber all over his mug and this totally innocent look on his face.

I can't recall the name I called him, as I reared back and chucked that golf ball sized rock at him from about forty yards away, but it was the last words he ever heard on this side of where ever milk stealin' calves go when they die. If I'm lyin' I'm dyin'.... but that durn rock hit him right between the eyes and down he went. I thought he was just knocked a little cuckoo, but after a few minutes of kickin', hollerin', and shakin' on him, I finally gave up. He just wouldn't wake back up, and we had butcherin' to do right in the middle of June.

I must have thrown a jillion rocks at critters through the years, and couldn't do that again if I tried, but I've never let loose of a rock since without thinking about the dumb milk-slobber look on that calf's face.

As the years wore on, Dolly matured and completely quit opening gates. She'd just jump where ever she wanted to go, and more than once we used her for a lead cow to get cattle across a bridge. One time in particular, we were trying to trail some yearlin's to town and got plugged up at the bridge right here at the house. We must have spent an hour or so trying to get them started, but finally gave up, and went to the corral for Dolly.

She knew the drill perfectly. The old girl just made two or three circles through the milling cattle and headed for town. They followed her right across that bridge like a bunch of soldiers. A half a mile or so down the road, with Dolly out in the lead and the yearlin's all strung out nice as you please behind her, she turns around right smack in the middle of the road, and marches back through them the way she'd come. The old girl walked right between the riders in the rear, recrossed the bridge, jumped over the corral fence, and went back to eating hay. She sure saved our bacon that time. We'd still be stuck at that bridge if it wasn't for her.

But, they say all good things must end. She finally got old, and lost one of the hindquarters of her udder to mastitis. A dairy man offered me $1300.00 for her, so I sold her. You'd o' thought I sold one of the kids, and it sure looked for a while like the cook was going to plumb quit this outfit.

For some reason she just didn't think that thirteen hundred bucks was enough money for a fourteen year old, three quartered, fence jumpin' cow. If the little woman of this outfit ever gets hauled into court I've got the perfect defense all figured out for her.

Insanity.

"He thinks he's sooo smart‼ Just **TRY** bein' a cow once."

66

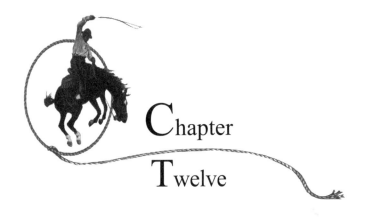

Chapter Twelve

One Seed Short

If you've got cattle…. they're gonna get out.
You can count on it. That's a law that must be written
down someplace. A friend of mine shared a little tale with
me the other day that needs repeatin'. He made me prom-
ise not to reveal his true identity, and after you hear the
story, I think you'll be able to see why.

The Donaldson family ran Black Angus cattle, and like
most ranchers, were pretty proud of their herd. They had
a good bunch of cows, but back in those days black cattle
weren't as big as they are now, and a big heifer at calvin'
time would weigh about 800 pounds or so. That seemed
to work out just fine… as long as you were a little selective about the bulls you used on them.

Right after breakfast one morning ol' Dad sent Tom
and Jack out to check the heifers. It was the middle of
June sometime, and breeding season was in full swing.

67

When the two boys got to the pasture, they found an unwanted visitor….. again. They'd had trouble with one of the neighbor's bulls and had chased him home several times, but the durn thing was back in again.

He was a big raw boned Charolais that weighed way over a ton, and probably had a birth weight of a hundred and twenty five pounds or so. To have him in with their heifers was just an accident waiting to happen. They'd never be able to have those calves.

The fence jumpin' bull belonged to the Bakers. They were pretty big operators that had a whole township of land in one chunk right over the fence and were always pretty quick to tell everyone just how much land they had and how successful they were. For them, a bull in with the neighbor's wasn't even an inconvenience. They had lots of bulls.

Ol' Man Donaldson had called and told them about the problem they'd had with the unwelcome visitor on several occasions, but the Bakers apparently had more pressing matters to attend to, and as a result the bull was back, and wouldn't stay out.

The young cowboys tied into the job at hand, but didn't have much luck. The boys were good hands and were pretty well mounted, but Mr. Bull was not very cooperative. He was enjoying the feminine companionship of a couple of the black beauties in his company, and had no intentions of going anywhere.

A ton of bull on the fight is nothin' to sneeze at. The bull won, and the boys went back home to break the bad news to Dad. The ol' man was furious. One thing the boys had learned through the years was to just stay quiet when Dad was on the prod. They didn't say a word, but just did as they were told and didn't ask any questions. Pa Donaldson jerked the cinch up on his big sorrel geldin' and had his rope down before they even got to the field.

The ol' man snagged the brute with his very first loop, but the bull had barely gotten the slack out of the rope when he wheeled around and came right back towards the horse. He had that sorrel gelding in his sights and murder on his mind. Dad managed to spur ahead enough that the bull missed him, but just barely.

You have to get this picture in your mind. There's a ton of mad Charolais bull headed south at 30 MPH with a rope around his neck, and ten feet of slack later, there's an irate cowboy dallied up on a 1300 pound horse headed west with that rope under his tail. Had the two not been connected, this story wouldn't be near this interesting.

What a wreck. Dad lived through it, but he was quite a while getting back to his feet and he didn't walk quite as straight when he finally wiped himself up off the ground. If it was actually possible, his mood had deteriorated even further.

The boys just THOUGHT he was on the prod before. He really had blood in his eye now. They headed back home for the pickup and more rope, with the boys just stayin' quiet and doing as they were told.

That old pickup was just hitting the high spots on the narrow prairie trail as Dad headed back out to the heifer field with the boys loping along behind. He ran the pickup tire up on the rope that was still around the bull's neck, and hollered at Jack to tie the knot end around the trailer hitch on the back.

"Now, heel that #$%$@," Dad yelled at Tom. A ton of bellerin' white bull was circling the pickup with Ol' man Donaldson tearin' an acre of prairie up with the pickup in four wheel drive.

Tom threw a loop on the rear end, and they soon had him stretched out. The boys were still in the dark as to how all of this was going to get the bull back in his own

69

pasture, but it wasn't long until they got the drift of the old man's plan.

As Dad stepped out of the pickup with his pocketknife in his hand, it was the first time they'd seen him smile all morning. It was the kind of grin that graces a tomcat's face just before he eats a big field mouse.

"Now, let the %#$@ up," were the instructions as the old man slipped his pocket knife back in his jeans. "Don't think he'll feel much like botherin' any heifers for a day or two."

The elder Mr. Donaldson had only done half a job of making a steer out of that bull, and although the boys feared it might kill him…. it didn't. Dad was right though; he sure didn't bother the heifers for a few days. A short time later they got him worked over into a field of cows where he wouldn't (or couldn't) do any serious damage.

70

Another strained phone call to the Bakers resulted in the permission to haul the bull to the sale barn on the next trip to town. The boys mixed him in with a few dry cows and Ol' Whitey got a one way ticket to the city.

The big successful land baron, Mr. Baker, was in the audience at the sale barn when his bull went through, and announced very loudly and proudly to the audience that this was a registered Charolais bull, and if anyone wanted him for breeding purposes that he would gladly pay for a fertility test. That's exactly what happened, and the fertility exam was ordered.

The Vet was grinnin' like a skunk eatin' onions as he gave Mr. Baker the news of why Whitey had flunked his test. Baker sent a glare at Jack and Tom that would burn the paint off the wall. Of course they didn't know anything about it.

Whitey was resold for hamburger. He'd just jumped his last fence, and for some strange reason the boys didn't have any further problems with white bulls bein' in with their heifers.

Bill Felton
He liked good Herefords, but he didn't like Ike.

Chapter

Thirteen

Walkin' To St. Paul

The culture of the West is changing, and I don't like it. After givin' this matter a little thought, I've come to the conclusion that the West has been in a constant state of flux for a couple of hundred years now, and the old guys never have liked it.

This really isn't anything new. The Indians didn't like it when us whiteys started movin' this way, the big cow outfits didn't like it when the homesteaders started farmin' up their free range, and probably nobody liked the fact that a lot of the homesteaders dried out and moved back to where they'd come from, owing money that would never be collected.

And the change continues. Our little rural schools that were once filled with country kids that actually got an education are no more, and the main streets of our home towns are drying up and blowin' away. Only one thing stays the same…. the old guys have never liked change.

One of the big culture changes came when the cattle industry began using trucks to move their livestock. For seventy five years or so, the railroad was the only viable means to transport our western cattle to the Midwest markets. I was too young to get in on riding a cattle train to market, but by the stories I've heard, I sure missed something.

There are folks that would probably argue that riding a cattle train wouldn't have anything to do with culture, but if you're a country boy that only gets into a little one horse town maybe eight or ten times a year, the chance to ride a train to a big city like Omaha or Sioux City would be the highlight of your year. That sure sounds like culture to me.

Here's a cowboy culture story from fifty years ago:

It was the fall of 1952, and The Great Northern Railroad had one of several cattle trains headed east on the highline to the stockyards in St. Paul. There were about twenty cowboys ridin' the caboose hooked to the rear of the train as it pulled from the loading point in Chinook, Montana.

It was the highlight of the cowboy social season. Several bottles of varying varieties of the very finest booze known to mankind were stashed among the suitcases of "town clothes" the boys had brought along with them. Of course the train had yet to turn a wheel before the first bottle was pulled from its hiding place. The cattle were all loaded and they were headed to St. Paul. That sounds like a good reason to celebrate to me. The slow moving train had barely cleared the siding on its way to the main rail line when the first jug was already history.

The first leg of the trip went to Minot, North Dakota where the cattle were unloaded to be fed, watered, and rested before resuming the remainder of the trek to the big market back East. The hot topic of conversation was the recent election. Dwight D. Eisenhower, the World War II hero, had recently trounced Adlai Stevenson in the presidential election.

We'll never know exactly how many of the boys had actually voted for Ike, but the election was over, the Republicans had won, and of course everyone on the train wanted to be on the winning side so they were all Republicans; everyone except Bill Felton.

Bill was a dyed-in-the-wool Democrat, and the rest of the guys gave him a pretty hard time all the way to Minot.

"I knew Ike was goin' to win," Eddy Olson quipped. "He led us boys in whippin' Hitler, an' beatin' up on a Democrat is nuthin' compared to that."

"I'd o' voted for a yella dog before I'd o' voted fer that bald headed &%$#," Bill fired back.

Eddy Olson

"Don't look like Stevenson has much hair either from the pictures I've seen," Howard Sayler piped up. "'Sides, that guy's nuthin but a lawyer, and he worked fer the Feds durin' Prohibition. Can't get much lower than that."

The madder Bill became in defending his Democratic convictions, the harder the boys laid it on. The odds in the caboose were 19 to 1, and the poor guy didn't have a chance. Other than the political discussion, the trip to Minot went as smooth as could be. The only casualties being several empty booze bottles and Bill's bruised ego.

The cattle were unloaded in Minot and put on good feed and water. The raucous merriment continued. After all, they were halfway there. Sounds like a good reason to celebrate to me.

The yearlin's were reloaded, the dwindling supply of liquid refreshments was replenished, and the cowboys reboarded the caboose. Their conversation resumed right where it had left off. In fact, the liberal ingestion of liquid spirits had probably deteriorated its tone.

"Maybe you WOULD vote for a yella dog before you'd vote fer a Republican, Bill. But dang it, you look smarter than that. Democrats ain't all bad. Truman was OK. He sure showed the Japs where the bear took a dump in the brush. Takes a lot of guts to pull the plug on one of them A bombs. Ike was just the best man that's all. Personally, I'd vote fer a monkey before I'd vote fer a %$#& lawyer. 'ats the trouble with you Bear Paw boys…. never learn to use yer heads."

That was the straw that broke the camel's back. Bill had his can full.

"By cripes I'll walk to St. Paul before I'll ride with a gang o' narrow minded %$#@ Republicans," Bill slurred, and out the back door of the caboose he staggered. Down the railroad tracks he tripped, whippin' himself down his hind leg with his hat and mutterin' under his breath.

I'm sure it's possible to walk from Minot to St. Paul. It's probably been done in the past, but it'll take a long time to get there headed down the tracks to the west like Bill was. The boys figured out a couple of things. They had to get Bill back on the train, and they didn't have much time.

Harry Olson tore out of the train after him. He finally got him stopped and turned around, but it took some mighty tall talkin' to get him back on the caboose. They'd nearly missed the train, and had barely gotten back aboard when it creaked out of the Minot siding and resumed the trip to the stockyards in St. Paul.

Many hours without sleep and the several gallons of missing whiskey resulted in the entire crew being dead to the world in their bunks by the time the train regained the main line. When they awoke in Minnesota, they had cattle to sell and all was forgotten and forgiven…. well, almost.

"I still don't like Ike," Bill muttered under his breath.

I wonder if ol' Bill **EVER** voted for a Republican?

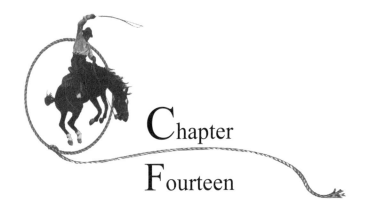

Chapter Fourteen

Itty-Bitty Kitty Crime

They say that crime doesn't pay. Sometimes that old sayin' is a little hard to justify when you see the way the government operates…. that's gotta be a crime, but it sure seems to be working for the folks with their hand in the till. I think I did see a lady get turned from a life of crime a few years ago, though. Maybe "woman" would be a better term…. she dang shore didn't act like much of a lady.

It was somewhere in between Thanksgiving and Christmas, and the little woman got a bad case of "shoppin' fever". It's a lot like the "shippin' fever" that the calves get in the fall, except there doesn't seem to be any cure for the stuff she gets. She had somehow convinced me that we should make a run into the big city for some serious Christmas shoppin'. I tried every excuse I knew, but she didn't buy any of them, so after an early round of chores, we got the kids on the school bus and loaded up for Great Falls.

As soon as I started the old car, I knew we had troubles. There was that pitiful "screech-thunk-thunk" sound that a cat makes when they go through the fan belt. The barn cats have a bad habit of crawling up on the warm engine when you shut an outfit off, and every once in a while get mixed up in the movin' parts when you start things back up.

"Dang it! There goes ol' Tommy," I muttered under my breath. It was too late. Poor ol' Tommy was history. I'll spare you all the gory details, but he was a real mess, and was now in several pieces. The wife was in tears. That was the kids' favorite cat. We were in a real rush as we had a long drive into town, and a lot on the schedule for the day, so I got one of those plastic shoppin' bags and scooped up what was left of the ol' boy, and put the bag on the floor of the back seat of the car. I'd have to deal with him later. We certainly didn't want the kids to come home and find him.

It's about a three-hour drive into Great Falls, so when we finally got there, we thought we'd stop for a cup of coffee before we began the day's business. We knew a lady that worked in a café downtown, so that's where we went. It was in sort of a seedy part of town, but the coffee was always good.

"You better lock the car. This isn't a very good neighborhood," the little woman cautioned.

"We haven't got a thing in here to steal," I brazenly replied as I stuck the keys in my pocket, and defiantly left the doors unlocked.

A spot by the window is always a favorite for curious country folks who like to see all the citified action, so we parked ourselves in a booth by the big plate glass windows to enjoy our coffee. On this particular day there was more action than even we expected. It wasn't long until we noticed an old girl coming down the street. She must have been a seasoned hand at the "five finger discount", because she spied our unlocked car doors from fifty feet away. Well, what do you know??... we had a front row seat to a real live crime. She walked up just like it was her car, and upon noticing the new shopping bag in the back seat, very calmly opened the door and picked up the bag.

"Kenny, do something!" my little bride exclaimed. "She's stealing out of **OUR** car."

"That's just ol' Tommy," was my calloused reply. "There really ain't much value to a dead cat. Besides, I didn't want to have to bury him anyway. If she wants him, she can have him."

We watched in amazement as the shameless old hussy walked right into the café like she owned the joint, sat down at the counter, and ordered a cup of coffee of her own. I'd give a thousand dollars for a videotape of what happened next. She took a big sip of her coffee, and nonchalantly reached down for the plastic shopping bag at her feet. Her curiosity had definitely gotten the best of her, and she had this driving inner need to discover the exact contents. After all, it was one of those pastel colored fancy bags the cook had gotten from a high dollar lady's store a couple of weeks before, so I'm sure her expectations were fairly high.

Without even looking into the bag, she thrust one hand clear to the bottom and into the middle of what used to be the inside of Tommy. The color her face turned is sort of hard to describe. It was somewhere in between purple and green. She took one quick look into the bag, gave a little sigh, and fainted dead away. Off the stool backwards she went. The first thing to hit the floor was the back of her head. It sounded like somebody dropped a watermelon.

We were the only ones that really knew what was going on, and I was havin' a hard time not laughin' out loud. I really don't think she was seriously hurt, but no one had any way of knowing she had just fainted, so the manager called 911. After all, here was an unconscious lady, with blood all over one hand. This was a real emergency. The ambulance came right away, and in no time they had her all loaded up on a gurney with an oxygen mask stuck over her nose. They couldn't seem to find the source of the blood.

"Don't forget her purse and shopping bag," the helpful waitress called.

The EMTs grabbed her purse, and sat the pink shopping bag containing poor ol' Tommy on her chest, and started rolling her out the door. I sure wish I could have been there when she came back around. That stolen shoppin' bag would have been the very first thing she saw.

Nope, crime dang shore doesn't pay.

Chapter Fifteen

John Wayne & Old Pete

There really isn't anything that can compare to growing up with the country all around you. Old Ma Nature can show you a lot if you'll just take the time to pay attention. Havin' the opportunity to live and work around various kinds of critters all of my life has been a real blessing, and havin' an animal buddy is one of the most essential parts of bein' a kid; at least as far as I'm concerned. That favorite pooch or some ol' ring boned plug can be the best pal that a little cowboy or cowgirl can have.

I remember lots of times growin' up when I'd get crossways with my folks, and not have a single place to go that was safe…. except maybe the barn. Absolutely no one would listen, or even give a doggone about my side of the story; at least no one but my animal buddies.

That's probably one of the reasons we're so diligent to make sure the kids that hang around here have a critter or two to play with and tell their troubles to. That's one of the problems with this dang modern society of ours. How in the dickens do you talk things over with some dumb video game? No wonder a lot of the kids nowadays have problems.

But, sometimes havin' pet-buddies can be a two-edged sword. There have been a lot of tears shed at the county fair market sales through the years. It's pretty tough to see the pal you've been sharin' secrets with all summer go to the butcher shop. I can show you more than one outfit around here where those tears have saved someone's buddy from the choppin' block and some rough, tough old rancher wound up pasturin' an old wether until he died of natural causes. But then…. there's a whole lot more to life than money.

Kelley and Kolton sort of have life figured out, I think. Ol' Pete had a lot to do with their budding cowboy philosophy, even if their theology might be a little tangled up. Let me explain here what I mean.

Ol' Pete was a burned out old rope horse that their Dad had gotten for them a few years ago, and he and those boys were a perfect fit. The boys were little and Pete was big, but that didn't make any difference. He'd really been around, that old boy, and loved those little guys to death. They could crawl all over him, and would wait 'til he got his head down in the oat pail, and then they'd climb on his head for a ride up to his back. Ol' Pete would lift his head just like an elevator, and they'd shinny down his neck and flip around on his back and they were in business.

Old horses are perfect for kids, but unfortunately sometimes their life expectancy isn't all that long. First you get old…. and then you die; at least that's the preferred order of things. Well, Ol' Pete didn't last as long as Dad had hoped, and they lost him last summer.

That's a pretty tough pill to swallow, and I'll tell you what, there were some awful long faces around that camp. It's sometimes hard to get your mind around something like that, 'specially for a kid, and the boys were desperately trying to make some sense out of the rotten hand that life had just dealt them. Sometimes life just ain't fair.

I think maybe they did get a handle on the big plan. At least the way they have it figured, it made things a little

easier to take. Dad had explained everything the best he could and hugged on 'em, and wiped away the many tears. A little time had passed, and the subject of losing their best friend hadn't come up for a while, so it seemed that the worst of the grief just might be over.

Then came the evenin' they were camped out in the yard with the cool summer breeze floating in the camper window and the stars shining

One of the Billmayer cowboys & Ol' Pete

brightly in the coal black sky. With all that quiet fresh air and extra time for reflection, those little heads got to thinkin' about "the good ol' days" and their favorite old pony.

"Dad?" Kolten breathed softly in the darkness, as he gazed up into the starlit sky.

"Yea, Kolten."

"Is Ol' Pete up in heaven?" his little voice starting to quiver with emotion.

83

"Shut up, Kolton!" his older brother interjected, afraid the tears would start all over again. "Don't talk about that stuff!"

Times like that really make a Dad earn his stripes, and he was diggin' deep for some answers to one of life's really big questions.

"Sure, I 'spose he is," Dad reassured the little guy, "Don't worry, Ol' Pete's OK."

"I sure miss him," the little voice quivered.

"Me too," answered his Dad, swallowin' the lump in his throat.

"Dad?" the older of the two questioned.

"Yea, Kelley."

"John Wayne's in heaven, ain't he?"

"He sure is," Dad answered, "... probably feedin' Ol' Pete right now."

There was a long pregnant silence as the boys pondered this new revelation. Somehow things seemed to be just a little better. If there was anyone that was good enough to trust with takin' care of Ol' Pete, it would have to be John Wayne.

The tiny rusty wheels were really turning in those little heads, and that's when one of them came up with an original theological concept to explain the order of things and the chain of command in heaven.

"So Dad?" one of the little cowboys asked with all sincerity. "First it's God, and then Jesus, and then John Wayne? Is that right?"

"Yea.... that's prob'ly the way it is," Dad answered his little buckaroos, glad that it was too dark for them to see his grin. "Just go to sleep now, boys.... don't worry. John Wayne's takin' good care of Ol' Pete."

Chapter Sixteen

Skunk Trappin'

*T*here have been more than a few times when neighbors have gotten a little crossways with each other. Folks have probably been feudin' and fussin' over fence and water and a hundred other things ever since the first cave man pulled on his Stetson and forked a horse. Usually both parties to those little disagreements think that they are the ones in the right and (of course) the problem is all the other fella's fault.

Then on the other hand there are folks that just set out to take advantage of their neighbors. Some of them view an opportunity to put the screws to someone as pure entertainment. If the guy over the fence is pretty well heeled with money to burn, they figure he's fair game. I can think of several of those kinds of deals.

Years ago there was a fairly well-to-do rancher up this way. He was a good operator and quite a wheeler-dealer.

Every time he'd take off to chase one of his big business deals, his hard scrabble neighbor would "even things out a little". Early in the morning as the big fancy car with the well dressed rancher pulled out over the hill, his hillbilly neighbor was letting down their common fence to herd his skinny cows across to graze on a little "free" grass.

By nightfall as the big Caddy came back up the road, the cows were back where they belonged and fence was back up like nothing had happened. I think everyone in the neighborhood knew what the deal was except for the fellow that got his grass borrowed. It was an arrangement that seemed to work for everyone, although I doubt the rich guy would have been very impressed with the situation had he known the whole score.

There was another situation sort of like that in the southern part of the state. Leo was quite a cowboy, and belonged to the old school of thought. He believed that God had created cows and grass (in that order) and that farmers and fences were just a pain in the neck that some idiot in Washington DC had come up with. Leo not only didn't fix much fence, but he really didn't care a great deal if his cows happened to be out on one of his neighbors.

This philosophy can lead to some real hard feelin's. Folks have been shot for a lot less than that. Several of Leo's neighbors had gotten their tail in a knot at his "open range" attitude, but he had quite a feud with one of them in particular.

This guy was a big farmer, and for some strange reason really didn't care to have fence climbin' cows constantly grazing off his wheat. They'd had words about it on several occasions, although it hadn't done a lick of good, and the feud had been building for a long time. Leo had been getting away with his operational style for years.... why should he change now?

After chasing the cows out of his grain for the umpteenth time, the farmer finally got his can full. One night about dark, he locked the cows up in his corral, and waited for Leo to come looking for them. It didn't take long. Leo might not have been much of a fencer, but he was a good cowboy, and knew full well where his missing cows were.

Dealing with a neighbor like Leo takes a little thinkin'. The farmer knew that he'd probably come down in the middle of the night to retrieve his missing stock, and in the process trample down another forty acres of wheat driving them home in the dark, so he put a chain and a padlock on the corral gate.

"He'll just cut that durn chain off," he thought to himself as he snapped the padlock shut, "....what I need to do is catch him in the act."

Confrontation with a hard nosed old timer like Leo really wasn't a pleasant thought, so the farmer came up with a plan. He set a bear trap in a shallow hole he dug by the corral gate, covered it with a little piece of canvas, and anchored the chain with an old car axle driven deep into the gumbo.

Bear traps are hard to set. Because of the intended prey, the springs are big and heavy and have to be compressed with clamps. A fella with his foot in one is pretty well caught and likely pretty well crippled. There's no escape.

Sure enough, a little after midnight, the still night air of the farmer's yard was pierced with the loud snap of the triggered bear trap, followed immediately by a painful yell and a blue streak of cuss words.

"Got 'im!" the farmer grinned as he got into his car to retrieve the Sheriff. It was the days before telephones, and twenty-two miles of dirt road lay between them and town. "He ought to be glad to see us by the time we back." Because Leo usually packed a six-shooter, going down to investigate the catch without the Law really wasn't a wise idea. A fellow with a bear trap on his leg is liable to have a real nasty attitude.

It was an hour and a half before the Sheriff and the farmer returned. He was right. Leo was dang glad to see them. The only thing that saved his leg was his high topped boots and shotgun chaps.

"Well, I'll be doggoned," the Lawman remarked as he walked over to Leo lying on the ground wincing in pain. "Now ain't this a new one? ….first time in my life I've ever seen a skunk caught in a bear trap."

"That puts me in mind o' that deal you got into on that plane we rode down to the Finals that time."

Chapter Seventeen

Look Where You're Steppin'

$\mathcal{D}$ick and Billy decided to take in the big National Finals rodeo down in Las Vegas a few years ago. It was their very first time, and they'd been planning and savin' their money for a year or so. They ordered the tickets for several of the performances as well as the big grand finale show, and were as excited as a couple of pups fightin' over an overshoe.

The sun was just peakin' over the rims as they drove into Billings to get on the plane. Those boys sure know how to get up in the morning, so they were there plenty early. That turned out to be an awfully good thing…. or else they just might have missed the plane completely.

"It's over three hours 'til the plane leaves," says Billy as they packed their war bags into the terminal. "I sure am thirsty…. I wonder if…."

"Me too," interrupted his partner, "Look-ee there at that sign."

It didn't take any time at all for those two country boys to get all settled down in the airport facility designed especially for thirsty, travelin' cowboys. Billy was particularly afraid of flyin'…. it being his first time and all, and although the price tag on the liquid courage dispensed at the only establishment they could locate was a little on the steep side…. after all…. they **WERE** on vacation, so slap a few back they did…. quite a few.

The security checkpoint proved to be sort of a challenge.

"Whadaya mean I can't take my pocket knife?" Billy belched in the grouchy looking guard's face, his breath faintly resembling the fragrance of fermented turpentine. "I don't never travel without my pocketknife."

"Security reasons, Sir," the guard snapped back crisply. "I know you certainly must be aware of the heightened security measures that must be taken since the terrorist incidents."

Billy's face was gettin' red and his temper was about to come uncorked. "Oh yea? Well, just how many cowboys with a pocketknife ever highjacked a airplane? Fer cryin' out loud can't you see we're Americans? It's all them fer-inners you need to worry about!"

It was an awfully good thing they were early, and that Dick's a good talker. The security guys were about to lock 'em both up. Somehow they smoothed it all over, and got on the plane in time…. but just barely. They were seated fairly close to the back of the plane, and a half a dozen rows ahead of them were a couple of women that they'd noticed when they loaded up. One of 'em was an unusually big old girl, and Dick made a comment as they sat down… just tryin' to get his buddy's mind off of whuppin' the security guard.

"Whoa.... did you see the size of that woman? She's big enough to drink diesel and wear mud flaps if she wanted to." Billy just snarled some unintelligible reply, replete with barnyard references to fer-inners.

As they started down the runway, Billy instantaneously forgot all about bein' mad, and the scared started to take over again. "Holy cow.... hope this sucker don't crash!" he gasped. " ... I ain't a-feared o' dyin', but I'd just as soon it weren't today."

He got a death grip on the side arms of the seat and squeezed his eyes shut, barely managing the courage to peak through the squint occasionally. They reached cruisin' altitude momentarily, and when the stewardess offered to bring him another barley sandwich.... suddenly everything was OK again.

The boys were about half way through their liquid brunch, when the large lady Dick had referred to earlier, got up and headed down the aisle to the restroom at the front of the plane. She was wearing a pair of those polyester pants.... you know, the kind with the stirrups in them. They frankly didn't flatter her more than ample frame.

"See!" says Dick to his pal. "There she goes!"

Billy craned his neck for a better look. "That ain't no girl.... looks like a Dodge dually with the tailgate down to me...." The boys had a good chuckle and went back to their brunch, excited to finally be on their way to the big rodeo.

Some experts maintain that there is a definite correlation between the copious consumption of liquids, and the frequency of the calls that Mother Nature issues for bladder relief. It must be true, because it wasn't long until Billy felt the urge to excuse himself to head for the facilities. He made his way down the aisle, visiting with everyone as he went, his fear of flying now totally under control. He flashed the pretty stewardess his very best smile, as he opened the door to the restroom and stepped in…. his eyes still riveted on the attractive lady.

Perhaps he should have been looking where he was going, for there seated in the four foot square restroom was the big lady that they'd seen head that way earlier… with the bottom half of her wardrobe down around her ankles. With his mind and eyeballs still on the stewardess, Billy didn't even see her, and stepped right in the middle of those huge polyester pants.

To say that the poor lady was a little startled with this sudden interruption of her biffy business, would probably be an understatement. She shrieked, reached for her pants, and stood up in one single motion. Billy's left boot slid down one leg of those huge britches, and was trapped there as his jeans leg was suddenly and completely enveloped in polyester.

He tried desperately to back out of this embarrassing situation, but with his leg stuck, he tripped and fell over backwards into the aisle, with three hundred pounds of enraged and partially exposed womanhood on top of him…. his boot firmly stuck in the stirrup of her britches. I've heard a lot of stories about gettin' hung up in a stirrup, but that beats 'em all.

It was an awful mess. For a minute there the poor guy didn't know if he was going to smother under that huge mound of infuriated femininity, or if she was just figuring on beatin' him to death. Either way, dyin' in a plane crash didn't look so bad right at the moment.

Somehow, he managed to live through it, and they went on to have a great time at the Finals. They've already got their tickets for next year. Billy says that there were a lot of new things to see in the big city, but one thing is just the same as back home in the barnyard.

"When you're wearin' your new boots…. a feller really needs to look where he's steppin'."

93

"Roses are red
and posies are pink

Cowboys ain't bad
once you get past the stink."

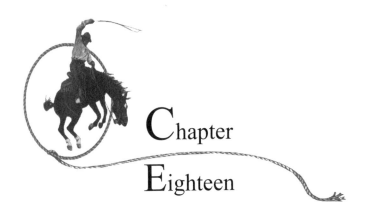

Chapter Eighteen

BRM... The Affectionate Solution

Boy, I sure don't seem to heal up as near as fast as I used to, and I'm afraid that it's a little more than just the natural aging process. It's clearly a result of a rather common form of abuse and misuse. These poor old joints are getting pretty stiff from all these years of harsh treatment, and when I can dig up the energy to turn my head, you'd swear to goodness that somebody was popin' popcorn. In fact, things have deteriorated to the point that I've even stooped to giving some thought to being a little more careful.... but on second thought its probably already too late. Perish that dumb idea. I guess I'll just keep going 'til I freeze down in a rockin' chair.... and that might not be all that far off the way I operate.

It's really not that I'm all that reckless, it's just that because of my twisted childhood, I have this mistaken idea that I'm somehow bullet proof. Parental over-affirmation will do that, you know. I've got what is known down at the Psycho Ward as a "Bull Rider Mentality" (BRM). Everyone who has somehow contracted this ailment, also suffers from an abnormally high SQ (Stupidity Quotient). There seems to be quite a bit of the stuff out here in the West. I think maybe the time I fell out of the barn loft on my head might have a little somethin' to do with it.

A guy afflicted with a malady of this sort can get himself in all kinds of jackpots. Like for instance the time I found a foot rot bull in the brush down on the creek. It was way past breeding season, and nearly time that we gathered them anyway. He really wasn't doing any harm down there, and even though it's been my experience that time usually heals that stuff about as well as a real vet sort of treatment, I just have to take him home so I can give him the proper medication.

Of course, he doesn't want to go. Those old boys can get a little cranky when they don't feel good anyway, and some joker is tryin' to chase them uphill out of the shade by their favorite water hole. A hand without BRM would just get a few cows and nurse him along with 'em, but rather than take the easy way out, Old Wild and Wooly me gets a kink in my tail and says, " Oh, yea? Try this on for size!" as I stick a loop on a ton of bull headed at a dead run downhill through some chokecherry bushes. I think I forgot to mention that my SQ had already assured me that my cinch was "Prob'ly tight enough…. Hurry, he's gettin' away!" You don't need much of an imagination to guess what happens next. I'll spare you some of the gorier details, but when I finally crawled back home that night, the cook thought I must have jumped off of a six story building into a cement mixer.

The scarier the endeavor appears to folks with normal brain waves, the greater the challenge to a guy suffering from BRM. I'm convinced that it isn't because the sufferer is sight impaired, impervious to pain, or that he's even overly courageous. In fact, he might actually be a real chicken at heart, but in every case I'm aware of, his SQ has him firmly persuaded in his frequently stepped on head that he's perhaps the only person in the universe that could achieve the objective before him without serious bodily harm. Unfortunately, sufferers just don't seem to posses the mental capacity to calculate the risk/reward ratio of the stupid stunt they're about to attempt. As a result.... well.... stuff happens.

Your Author working on his BRM in the 60's

I may very well be the nation's leading expert on BRM.... by default. Most of the others that caught it, have long since violently passed on to their reward (or punishment, dependin' on your theology), or they're just too durn bashful to speak up. So, as the official spokesman for BRM Anonymous, I feel compelled to take some time away from the twelve step program we're developing to help set the record straight.

97

We get a bad rep with a lot of folks for being reckless, wild, crazy, dumb, etc., etc., when it is really the positive aspects of our personality that get us into the mess in the first place. Sometimes a BRM sufferer will tie into a little project that even someone "normal" would attempt. The big difference here is that when the deal turns south, and the normal guy pulls out, we fail to ascertain the potential pain and suffering. The SQ factor kicks in, and we just pull our hat down and pour on the spurs. The result of which, assuming we're successful, is additional over-affirmation of our bullet proof-ness. That only makes things worse when the next deal comes up.

Unfortunately, about half the time, the result is more like the normal guy without the cranial constipation of a BRM sufferer thought it would be, and we have another wreck on our hands. We either wind up being a hero for accomplishing an impossible task single-handedly, or more often, look like an idiot.... with our clothes in tatters and hide missing on every exposed surface.

So you see, some of the wild reckless characters in your life really may have a legitimate explanation for their behavior. Most of them don't even know they have a problem, much less the source, and because of the mental deficiencies already mentioned, wouldn't admit it if you took the time to make an explanation.

Although BRM unfortunately has no cure, research scientists have developed a simple method to alleviate its symptoms. It appears to be relatively easy to control with an increased level of fervent feminine affection and companionship. Ladies.... please take the time to hug a cowboy today. You may be their only hope, and their health and safety depends on it.

98

Chapter Nineteen

Electronic City Livin'

I just helped Doc and Agnes move back out to the ranch. They tried their little fling at city life, but it just wasn't for them… they couldn't live like that. I think they must have made it three or four years in town, which is probably a lot better than I could have done. It all started a few years ago with Agnes getting tired of the acre and a half she had to mow around the yard, and Doc fed up right to his ears with the BLM's baloney. But the straw that broke the camel's back was when Doc's old horse spooked and ran off with him. Down through the junipers they went. He got him rode to a stop, but there wasn't a spot on him that wasn't skinned up.

"Dang it, Agnes. I've had it. Murphy's have been tryin' to lease this place for years, and I'm givin' them a call. I can flip hamburgers in town and make as much money as we're makin' here, and a durn site easier."

"I'm too tired to argue with you. Besides, settin' a spell sounds pretty good to me, too," was the exhausted answer Agnes gave him.

A little over a week later they were all packed up and headed into town. Doc landed a job with the railroad that paid him a couple of month's wages every week, and about all he had to do was show up. He bought Agnes a brand new house in one of those developments that had a circular sort of a street. It was so much nicer than the old ranch house that it wasn't even funny, and the yard seemed like it was only about the size of a postage stamp. Agnes thought she'd died and gone to heaven.

It wasn't very long until their troubles started. The railroad not only didn't work Doc very hard, but after only eight hours, they MADE him leave. What in the dickens is a fellow 'sposed to do for the rest of the day? A guy that's used to working from sun to sun has some serious adjustin' to do. He went home and put his feet up for a day or two, but that got old pretty quick, and it wasn't very long until he started getting on the cook's nerves. He tried golf, but knockin' that little ball off in the brush and then looking for it for an hour or so really didn't turn his crank either.

The inevitable happened. Doc took to drinkin'. His excess really wasn't intentional, but that stuff has a way of sneakin' up on you, and it led to an even worse problem. All the houses on their whole street were built at the same time, with the same plans…. by the same guy, who painted them all the same color. Findin' his house in the daylight with his head screwed on straight was hard enough, but at midnight after a long evenin' downtown, it was nearly impossible.

There were at least a hundred of them that all looked the same. The only sure-fire way that he could find his way home was to just start walkin' down the street, tryin' the doors. All the town folks locked theirs, and Doc and

Agnes hadn't picked up that bad habit yet, so when he found a door unlocked, he knew he had the right one.

He was explaining his method to one of his crony's at work, and the guy had a fit.

"What if the cops see you headed down the street tryin' all the doors? They'll lock you up so fast it'll make yer head spin. You need to get yourself a garage door opener.... that's what I did. I couldn't find our house either. You just drive down the street real slow and keep your finger on the button. When a door opens, you got the right place."

Now that made a lot of sense, so Doc invested in one of those new-fangled electronic garage door openers, and it worked like a charm. He got the right house ever time. Things were pickin' up. This city livin' didn't seem so bad.

Then a few months ago, the O'Brien's moved in next door. They were nice enough folks, and good neighbors. I think the old man was a truck driver or something, and Doc and him hit it off just fine. Little did they know that trouble lurked right around the corner.

O'Brien was a drinker too, but unfortunately hadn't gotten on to the garage door opener trick yet. About midnight one Thursday night, he wandered home a little worse for wear, and accidentally got the wrong house. The key didn't seem to fit very well, but luckily the door opened anyway. As fate would have it, it just happened to be Agnes' bed he crawled into. Now, Agnes knew that Doc was downtown, so she didn't think anything was strange when a drunk stumbled up the stairs and crawled into bed with her. She just gave him the same old cold shoulder that she always did, and didn't even bother to wake up.

About an hour or so later, Doc got home. It's sure a good thing he's an understanding sort and not prone to violence. His first clue something was amiss was when he stumbled over the boots in the hall. He flipped on the light, and the rest is history. The exact exchange of words were not recorded…. probably thankfully. Agnes was mortified. She might have gotten used to sleepin' with a drunk, but this was ridiculous. That was the last night she didn't lock her door, and the house went up for sale the very next day.

Boy, they're glad to be back on the ranch again…. that city livin' is for the birds, and you know something?

Doc ain't had a drink since. 🎩

"Now, Dick I can understand a lady lockin' her door, but quitin' drinkin?? Don't that sound a little EXTREME?"

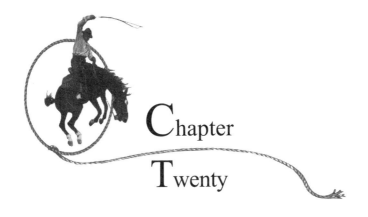

Chapter Twenty

Ed Ain't Much of a Cowboy

The real modern day cowboy is sort of a strange cuss…. a mixture of myth and reality, of truth and bull pucky. He's larger than life to many of his city admirers, and if the face that looks at him from the mirror happens to occasionally appear a little battered, he's still none the less firmly convinced that he is indeed bullet proof.

What makes a real cowboy anyway? It sure isn't the clothes, although that's got somethin' to do with it. Years ago I was standing next to an old hand in front of the chutes at a rodeo, when this ridiculous lookin' character walked past. Some of his "friends" had paid his entry fee in the bull ridin', and then double-dog dared him to do it. It was back when the hippy deal was in full swing, and this ol' kid had bought into it hook line and sinker. With his long hair and love beads, he was a real sight for sore eyes.

The ride didn't take too long, and everyone got a good laugh... except for the old timer I was standing by. He was just disgusted. "Not everyone can ride like a cowboy, but there ain't no durn excuse for not lookin' like one."

A real hand can usually always tell another one. Even the right clothes won't fool 'em.... they can tell a phony ever' time, and I'm not exactly sure how. I've tried to think about what it might be, but I can't seem to put a handle on it. Maybe it's just the way they wear their hat, or the way they walk, I don't know. Here's a couple of lines I stole from one of Wally McRae's poems:

"...it may be their posture, or bearing
Or the confident look in their eye"

Unfortunately, the rest of the world isn't blessed with that degree of insight. Their perception of real cowboys comes from what they've seen in the movies, or on the Nashville Channel.... baloney in living color. The movies portray fancy flowerdy shirts, tight pants, and silver Mexican spurs with four-inch rowels, where the Nashville version shows a fruitcake with his shirt unbuttoned halfway to his belt buckle with a half a dozen gold chains hangin' around his neck, and sporting an earring or two. Of course both of these fictitious characters are topped with a big hat, (that should be again' the law) and both pile fertilizer on the misconception of what a cowboy really is.

That gets me to a little story that happened to Ed Solomon. I heard this second hand, and the guy I heard it from has been known to lie right through his teeth, so I'm going to have to fill in the blanks a little. I could have called Ed and gotten the whole story straight from him, but I think you'll probably like my version better anyway, so if you prefer the real scoop, maybe you better just ask Ed next time you run into him.

Now, I'm not blowin' smoke at you. If there's some-one that's is, was, and always will be a cowboy, it's Ed Solomon. He's got a rep for raising good horses and is always mounted about as well as a man can be. He's owned a livestock auction barn and traded a lot of cattle, as well as running his registered quarter horses and a cow herd, and has been in demand as a pickup man at every rodeo for a thousand miles in every direction for the last fifty years or so. If there's one thing they could chisel on his stone when he rides over the Big Divide, that every good hand I know would agree with, it would be this:

"He's A Cowboy"

Ed Solomon

Well, Ed was draggin' a trailer and a couple of horses up a lonesome piece of highway one day, when he hap-pens upon this car with New York plates that was stopped alongside the road. He couldn't just drive on by, even if he'd wanted to. It would have been a violation of the Cowboy Code not to stop to help someone that needs it. That seems to be another thing that some of our city cousins have forgotten.

What should our knight in well-worn chaps find, but a pair of elderly motorists with a flat tire. It was a doctor and his wife on a sight seeing trip in our fair state, and the gentleman of the group was pretty inept at roadside emergencies. He might have been a real whiz at brain surgery or maybe lung transplants, but he couldn't even seem to find the jack.

Ed had them jacked up and the tire changed in nothin' flat, the whole time keeping them entertained with his good-natured range wisdom. The doctor just looked on in awe as this crusty prince of the plains took complete command of the situation, all the while taking mental notes and asking questions about his life, his horses, his hat and neck scarf, and a thousand other things that most any second grader around here would know. He also commented on the cuttin' horse spurs that dangled from the heels of Ed's boots. I think he puts them on when he buys a pair of boots, and takes them off when he gets a new pair.

The doctor's wife, on the other hand, sat quietly in the car, tightly clutching a can of pepper spray, which was partially hidden beneath her purse. She stayed quiet as a mouse, and peeked out occasionally through the window she had rolled down a couple of inches.

"Muriel, look! Our first day in Montana, and we meet a real cowboy!" the doctor called to his wife. Muriel peered cautiously out of the car again and set her gaze firmly on Ed's spurs with their small round one-inch brass rowels.

"He's not a real cowboy!" she replied indignantly, calling upon her vast movie going cowboy experience, "See… you can tell by those little bitty wheels on his spurs."

106

Chapter Twenty-One

Sniffin' On the Wrong Track

$\mathcal{R}$ed Tompkins is a natural born hunter and outdoorsman. He's from down in the Ozark Mountains someplace, and other than dabblin' in the moonshine business a little, hunting and fishing is about all he's ever done. He's some kind of distant kin folk to Leon Parker, and Leon has been tellin' him Montana hunting stories for years.... all true, I'm sure. Well, it really got ol' Red's mouth waterin' to bag a big mule deer and an antelope, so one fall he drove his old pickup up here, and Leon took him huntin'.

They had a great time for two or three weeks, and Red was just fixin' to head back south, when Leon suggested that he hang around a little while longer until they got a little snow, and they could run some cats down in the Missouri Breaks. This was the first time the subject had come up, and Red just couldn't wait to hear more.

"What kinda cats are they, and how do you run 'em?"

"Mountain lions…. they're awful bad to eat horses. Pete Swanson's got a bunch of hounds, and I've been out with him lots of times. I heard that he just got in a new one or two from back in Tennessee or someplace that are really s'posed to have good noses." That was all the arm twistin' that Red needed to stay. He'd used hounds on about everything that a feller could down in the Ozarks, and the chance at a big cat hunt was just more than he could turn down. He was stayin'.

"Where's Pete live? I'd shore like to take a look at his dogs."

"He's got a little cabin down in the Little Rockies by the Big Hole."

"I thought you said the Big Hole was down by Dillon someplace."

"Not THAT Big Hole. Folks around here call that hole out by Pete's the Big Hole. It's a limestone cave that they say ain't got any bottom."

A couple of weeks later they got a little skiff of snow, so they called up Pete and made arrangements to take the dogs down to see if they could pick up a track. They agreed to meet up at Pete's place about mid morning, but Red just had to see this big hole that Leon had been tellin' him about, so they took the trail up the coulee and went into Pete's the back way.

"His place is up through those trees," said Leon as he pulled the pickup off the trail. "The Big Hole is right over there. Come on, I'll show you."

Red wasn't very impressed. There before them was an unobtrusive nondescript hole in the ground that was about fifteen or twenty feet across.

"THAT'S the famous Big Hole? What's so great about that? We got holes in Arkansas that would make that little thing look like a gopher dug it."

108

"They say it ain't got no bottom," answered Leon as he chucked a rock off in the hole. "Listen." They both cocked an ear, but couldn't hear a thing. "See, I told you."

Red wasn't that easily convinced, so he picked up a bigger rock and heaved it into the hole. They both listened quietly, but they never did hear a sound. "I'll be doggoned," says Red. "We need to find something bigger to throw in there. There's no such thing as a hole with no bottom." They both took off to find a bigger bottom finder.

"Here we go," yelled Leon. "Help me with this railroad tie." He'd found the old tie on a little trail that led into the woods towards Pete's place. They each grabbed an end of the tie, and on the count of three, lobbed it off into the Big Hole, and then turned their heads to listen.

There was no sound at all, until they heard a hound bay like he'd just hit a hot trail. The sound was comin' from behind them up the trail towards Pete's. As they turned around to look, they couldn't believe what happened next. There was a big blue hound coming their way on a high run…. bayin' his lungs out. To their surprise he didn't

109

slow up a bit, but ran right in between them and with a giant leap, jumped right off into the middle of the hole. He was still bayin' as he went out of earshot.

It was the durndest thing either one of them had ever seen. They just stood there lookin' two-eyed at each other, desperately trying to figure out what had just happened, when they heard the leaves rustle on the trail behind them. It was Pete.

"You guys seen Ol' Blue? I'da swore I heard him hit a trail. There's no cats around here. I wonder what in the world's got into him?"

The boys were buyin' time, trying to figure out how to break the news to poor ol' Pete, so they began to ask a few questions about what this missin' dog looked like.

"He's a big Blue Tick hound that I just got from Tennessee. I was afraid that the other dogs would clean up on him, so I had him back up there in a patch of brush," Pete said, motioning back up the trail. "Wonder how he got loose? ….I thought I had him tied real good to that railroad tie."

Chapter Twenty-Two

Sellin' Stuff Twice

 $\mathscr{G}$ irls are gonna be my downfall. I've noticed some of the things they've been able to pull off over the years, and I've come to the conclusion that there's a lot of untapped potential that could be exploited by someone with an innovative criminal mind. Here's where my problem lies. (You know that famous old saying… "A Criminal mind is a terrible thing to waste.") Although I've so far been able to resist the temptation, it's possible that I could have actually done some hard time for stealin' bum lambs a few years ago, and it was all a girl's fault. Actually, there would have been two girls to blame, my wife and Peggy Werk.

Peggy lived down the river a ways from us, and one summer she had a whole pen full of bucket calves. It was gettin' along towards fall, and she had them all weaned and turned out to run in the hay meadows. They came up to the barn twice a day just like clockwork for their daily ration of grain and ear scratchin'. Of course she didn't bother to brand 'em. She knew them all by name, and they were totally convinced in their little bovine brains that she was their real mother. Usually that works out just fine, but poor ol' Peggy got in a jam when one of the neighbors shipped his calves and hers just happened to get on the truck bound for the sale barn. She got home in time for the chores one evening and.... NO BABIES.

There is an old saying, "Hell hath no fury like a woman scorned." That may be true, but if the woman happens to be a mother, and the scornin' has something to do with one of her babies.... look out. It didn't take any time at all for her to get to the bottom of the problem, and figure out where her calves had gone. She called Jack Siebrasse, the District Brand Inspector, on the phone and really filled his ear full. Jack was a good, honest, and compassionate man, but there was only so much he could do.

"If they're not branded, there's no way you can prove they belong to you, even if you know they're yours. You should have branded them, and then you wouldn't be in this mess," Jack told her as sympathetically as possible.

"If they were still on the cows, and the cows had my brand, would that matter?" asked Peggy, getting desperate.

"Sure, but you said they were orphans."

"They USED to be orphans, now I'm their Mother."

After a check of the records at the sale barn, it was determined that the little lost babies had wound up on a truck bound for a feedlot in Shelby, nearly 150 miles away. Peggy convinced Jack to go with her to the lot, and she'd prove to him they were her calves. She carefully gave a detailed description of each one, and although the inspector was a little on the leery side, he decided to give the lady a chance to substantiate her claim. Unfortunately, when they arrived at the feedlot, they found about six hundred head of bawlin', freshly weaned calves runnin' around in circles.

"Just pull the pickup and trailer in the middle of the pen, and I'll load 'em up. I think I see one of them already."

"Here Flossy, Here Bingo, Here Pookey. (Pookey is the one that thought he was Bodacious, but I already told you that story.) WOO-hoo-HOOooOOoo!" Peggy hollered as she rattled an old bucket. Every one of her babies jumped right in the back of the trailer to get their ears scratched, and they were all accounted for.

"I'll be doggoned," says Jack. "I'd say those were your calves all right."

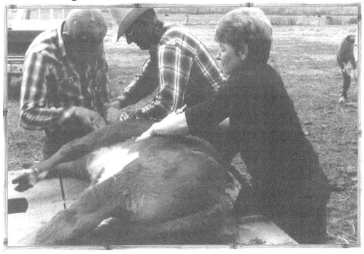

Peggy at Paul Ramberg's Brandin'

Peggy got her calves back, and the whole neighborhood had a good laugh. Now, that remarkable turn of events really didn't affect us at all at the time, and everything was fine at our place until the little woman sold her bum lambs a few weeks later. Back when the big outfits around here were in the sheep business, they used to give the bums away for free, and because she had an indentured servant with two or three milk cows (me), she felt the bum lamb business was a natural fit for our operation. She had a little different call than Peggy's. Hers went sort of like this: BABY, BABY, BABYEEEeeeeeEEEE. (This really loses a lot in the translation... you actually need to hear this to properly appreciate it.)

That fall she sold her seventeen bums to the Milk River Lamb Pool. They received lambs on about four dates throughout the fall, and because hers were nice and heavy, she shipped on their very first one. A couple of days later we were headed into town, and I'll be durned, but there grazin' on the sugar beet tops in the field behind ol' Red Steinmetz's barn were at least a thousand head of lambs.

Looky there!" says the criminally minded member of our family. "I'll betcha those are the lambs that the Pool just bought. Quick! Holler at 'em, and see if yours 'll come. If Peggy can do it, so can you. We'll just get 'em to follow us home, and we can sell the little buggers again the next time they ship." (Actually, I was kiddin'.... I think. For a cowboy to risk doin' hard time for stealin' bum lambs, takes even less brains than I've got.)

Mama wouldn't have anything to do with it. Of course, always bein' up for a challenge, I slowed up the old pickup, rolled down the window, and did my very best feminine impersonation of a "bum lamb callin'". After all, I'd been hearin' it all summer, so I even had the real high soprano part down pretty good. I just let 'er fly and waited to see if the bums would cut themselves out of the bunch. BABY, BABY, BABYEEEeeeeeEEEE.

Unfortunately, unbeknownst to me, there was a sheep-herder settin' with his back to a fence post not thirty feet from me. He stood up real slow and turned around, givin' me the strangest look you ever saw. Just like a flash of lightnin', I rolled up the window and kicked that old pickup in the tail. I think the danged old pervert thought I was talkin' to him.

Chapter
Twenty-Three

Smarter Than They Look

*D*ick and Billy live at the end of twenty miles of gumbo road. Their place is really a sight for sore eyes, and they seem to spend a lot of time just trying to figure out how to stay in business. They've tried nearly everything. When the Tomcat neuterin' deal didn't work out, they gathered and sold petrified dinosaur artifacts for a while... but then the Sheriff offered them free room and board unless they agreed to knock it off, and they were right back where they started. The boys actually thought they were on to something that time.

"I think we need to get us one of them big trucks that bend in the middle and a 'possum belly trailer," Dick remarked one mornin' at breakfast. "Ever'body knows those truckers is all rich. We sure need to perk the income up around here a little bit."

"Yup. Good idea," Billy hiccupped as he popped the top on his fourth barley sandwich. "Where ya gonna get the money fer that? One o' them big rigs 'd probably cost ten thouzan bucks."

"We'll have to borry it, I s'pose," Dick answered as he dialed up the banker. Billy left Dick to his phone call and went outside to answer the one he'd just received from Mother Nature.

"What 'd he say?" Billy asked, as he came back in, slammin' the bunkhouse door.

"He said we could have the money, but he's comin' out this afternoon to count the cows. He was sort of dragin' his feet, so I accidentally told him we had a couple o' hundred more than we really do. He just wants to count 'em to make sure."

"Oh, that's just great," Billy slobbered. "Now what are we gonna do?"

"I'll take care o' him, and do all the talkin'," was Dick's confident reply. "Don't worry 'bout a thing. You go take the fence down back behind Rocky Butte and run that bunch of Harmon's cows in with ours. Then just throw the whole works together, and trail 'em down the fence by the county road. I'll get in the banker's outfit with him and set him out on the road. He can get a good count from there, and we'll still have plenty of time to cut Harmon's back out before dark. Cows is cows to a banker.... he won't know the difference."

The plan worked like a charm, and the boys got their loan, but ten thousand dollars really didn't buy much of a truck and trailer. They had to jump start it every morning, and the brakes weren't too good.... but then it fit right into the rest of their operation. After getting a few loads to haul from the neighbors, it looked like they might even make a buck or two. That's when things headed south.

The boys decided to haul a load of their yearlin' steers to Billings to the sale barn, and the trip turned into a real

116

nightmare. The day started off well enough.... the old truck started all by itself, and they had it all loaded before daylight. After grabbin' a six-pack for breakfast on the road, Dick took the wheel and away they went. Around nine o'clock in the morning, the warm morning air was suddenly invaded by a bunch of blue flashin' lights and a siren.... right behind the truck.

"Oh no!" gasped Dick, "It's Bull Frog.... the D.O.T. man!" (Everyone called him Bull Frog because of his fat little double chin, his big belly, and his pointy little face with the big wide mouth.)

"What's D.O.T. mean?" hiccupped Billy.

"Just shut up Billy. Don't say nothin'.... and fer cryin' out loud, hide the rest of yer breakfast!" Billy shoved the open bottle into his jeans, as Bull Frog motioned the boys and their truck onto the wide shoulder of the road.

Now, Bull Frog was a rookie. He was proud as punch of his brand new uniform, and his shinny new badge. His pants were tucked in the top of his combat boots, and with his thumbs stuck in his new gun belt, he swaggered up beside the truck.

"Just keep your seats, gentlemen," Bull Frog ordered, full of authority. "I'll need to weigh your load with my portable scales." He cast a suspicious eye at the dangling tail light wires on the way back to his vehicle. Dick was nervous, and Billy was mad.

"Ain't none of his dad blamed business how many steers we got in here. They're our steers, an' this is our truck."

"Billy!"

"Ok, ok," Billy burped. "I'll keep my mouth shut."

It wasn't long until the officer had determined that the boys were ten thousand pounds overweight, and along with no tail lights, had a list of other infractions as long as your arm. His self importance was now at an all time high. Bull Frog really seemed to enjoy having a new victim in a tight spot. He put one big shinny combat boot up on the

117

hub of the front wheel, and began to gleefully write in his brand new ticket book.

It was a warm humid morning, and the flies were extra bad. The officer was constantly waving them off his fat little face.

"The flies are sure bad this year, aren't they," remarked Dick, trying to make a little conversation and hopefully lessen his fine.

"Them 's Circle Flies," Billy piped up.

"Circle Flies?" inquired the officer.

"Yup," slobbered Billy. "Only place you ever see 'm is circlin' round a horse's rear end."

The rookie officer bristled, his fat face turned a brilliant red, and he began to shake all over.

"Insulting an officer of the law is a crime, sir," Bull Frog sputtered. "Are you calling me a horse's hind end?"

"Billy!" Dick interrupted, as he flashed his partner that shut up or I'll kill you look.

"Oh, no sir. We have entirely too much respect for your uniform and for the law to say anything like that."

"Very well," the officer continued, suspiciously eyeing the pair as he continued writing on the second page of his new ticket book. Soon he was again waving and swatting the flies swarming around his head. Billy began to chuckle over in the passenger seat of the truck. His amusement was fairly subdued at first, but before long his liquid breakfast began to take control and he was nearly roaring with laughter.

"What do you find so humorous?" the officer asked indignantly.

"Dad was right!" Billy roared, no longer able to contain himself. "They're a whole lot smarter than they look…. it's dang hard to fool a Circle Fly!"

118

Chapter Twenty-Four

You Gotta Bury The Hide

Pinky Malone used to run some cows down by the Missouri River. Some of that country is purty dang rough, and it's fairly easy to come up a few head short, so Pinky just sort of figured that into the cost of doin' business.

It really came as no surprise when he jumped a big yearlin' steer out of the brush that he'd missed the year before while he was on the fall gather. He already had a half a dozen cows and calves or so that he was trailin' up a coulee, so by rights, adding the steer to the little bunch he already had should be a snap. Not this old boy. He'd only seen a human bein' once before, and the trick that guy had pulled on him with a rope and a pocketknife was still emblazoned deep in the recesses of his memory.

He threw his tail over his back, and down the coulee to the rough country he went, with Pinky in hot pursuit. Bein'

119

pretty well mounted, our cowboy caught up to him all right, but turnin' him around was out of the question. Visions of an instant replay of the last encounter he'd had with a guy with a big hat and a rope made Mr. Bovine fairly determined to put as much real estate between himself and good flat ropin' ground as possible. Besides, it was at least five miles of tough trail between where they were and a spot flat enough to get him loaded. So, although he sure hated to, Pinky had little choice but to wave goodbye as the steer "went driftin' down the draw".

In the ensuing years that crazy steer got even older, and smarter, and wilder, until he got to be five or six years old. By now he was a big old bruiser that was instantly on the fight at the first sight of a rider, and got the buffalo on more than one good hand. He was big enough to back it up, too.

Luck, whether it's bad or good, only seems to last just so long. The old steer ran out of his when he wound up in a bunch of cows belonging to one of the neighbors, and got himself into a corral before he knew what had happened. Pinky was tickled even pinker than he normally looked when he got the call.

"We shipped out of the old horse corral down at the cow camp yesterday, and left him locked up. Boy he's on the fight. We knew you've been tryin' to get him for years, but you better just butcher him down there. He's liable to hurt somebody."

"Gee thanks, Art," Pinky answered. I'll get some help and go down first thing in the morning. I really appreciate it. I'll leave the hide on the corral fence for your trouble." (That was back in the days when a big steer hide would still bring a few dollars.)

He got Smiley Stuart to give him a hand and they got everything together for the big day. They cut three heavy fir poles about twenty feet long and got a block and tackle, and gathering all the other butcherin' stuff they'd need, loaded up a gun or two and headed for the cow camp.

"How big IS this steer?" Smiley wondered out loud.

"Oh, I don't know. He's five or six years old. He probably weighs sixteen or seventeen hundred I s'pose."

"That's what I was afraid of. We're gonna need some help. There's no way we can hoist up that big o' critter."

"You know, I think yer right," Pinky answered as he turned the pickup around. They stopped down at Fort Belknap, and picked up a couple of big strappin' young fellas to help, and with them sittin' on top of the poles to hold 'em in the back of the box, they headed south for their prize.

An hour or two later, they got to the remote cow camp. There was a little grove of trees and a big sandstone rock that sheltered their arrival from the corral containing their intended victim. Pinky shut off the pickup in the trees, and signaling everyone to be quiet, took his rifle and snuck up to peek over the rock. Everyone knows that the meat from a riled up critter sure isn't as good as that from one that's caught sleepin', and as wild as that steer was, his plan was to pop the ol' boy before he even knew anyone was around.

The plan was a complete success. The steer was laying in the middle of the corral chewin' his cud, totally unaware that his appointed hour had come. He didn't even know what hit him. Making a tepee tripod out of the poles and hoisting the beef up on it, they quickly finished up their chore. After wrapping the quarters in old bed sheets, the two husky kids loaded them into the back of the pickup, as the older guys drug the heavy hide over the pole corral to leave it behind just as Pinky had promised. The whole operation had taken less than an hour, and they were soon headed back up the trail towards home.

"Those boys really knew what they were doin," Smiley

121

commented as he motioned toward the two riding in the back with the beef. "I didn't think we'd get it done this fast."

"Neither did I," Pinky answered smiling smugly at the sweet victory of finally coming out on top of a battle with the old steer. Unfortunately he must have forgotten to tell the boys the whole story of why he'd wanted to sneak up on the beef, because they hadn't gotten a hundred yards from the corral, when the boys in the back started yellin' and pounding on the top of the cab with their fists.

"Stop! Stop! Stop! We forgot to bury the hide!"

The fellas in the front about split a gut…. laughing 'til they thought they'd die. Apparently it was the first butcherin' those two boys had ever attended that didn't include a hide buryin'.

"Now me…. I'm lookin' forward to buryin' a cowboy's hide."

Chapter Twenty-Five

Not Such a Lucky Strike

I'm sure having trouble figurin' out all the flap that folks are making about this racial profiling. It just plain doesn't make sense to me. If several airplane loads of one-eyed cowboys had been responsible for all that terrorist stuff, it would only seem logical that I might be a prime suspect. As a result I could probably expect to look forward to having my old pickup pulled over for something besides just missin' mud flaps or expired license plates.

Now shootin' all one-eyed cowboys on sight might be a little extreme. That could tend to make even a squeaky clean, law abidin' type like me sort of nervous, but pullin' a guy over to find out who he is and what he's up to sure looks legitimate to me. If you see a couple of Mexican lookin' guys steal the hubcaps off your car, why in the world would you suspect a redheaded Irishman. On the other hand, if it was a redheaded Irish lookin' dude that was observed galloping away from the scene, checkin' up on the redheads just might make sense.

Cowboys must be a little behind the times, I guess. Say for instance you've got a nice herd of purebred Angus cows, and one of them comes in with a big Charlois calf. It would take a pretty poor cowman to beat the dickens out of the neighbor next door with Hereford bulls, wouldn't it? Suspectin' the guy down the road with the field full of white ones and a lousy fence might be lot better place to look.

Times sure have changed. In our fair little community during World War I, there were a lot of German immigrants. That made some of the town fathers more than a little nervous. Some of them were suspected of being a little too attached to the old country, and therefore having Anti-American sympathies. They were considered a threat to the country and consequently to the safety of the community. A Committee was formed that compiled a list containing the names of all those of German descent, and various members of the committee were assigned to investigate suspect individuals.

As far as I know, the Committee really didn't do anything out of hand…. although I doubt if the ACLU would have approved of the method they used on one outspoken German gentleman. He was required to crawl on his hands and knees for a block down Main Street and then to kiss the American flag and swear his allegiance. It's too bad those old boys aren't still around. We could send 'em out to Hollywood to clean that mess out. Everyone should have a choice…. after all, this is America. You can either swear allegiance, or be furnished a one-way ticket to Baghdad. It wasn't too long ago that the human shield business was boomin' over that way.

On the other hand, a lot of Japanese families really got a raw deal during the Second World War. Many have argued that it was a gross overreaction, and it well could have been. Although desperate times sometimes require desperate action, I doubt if their relocation would have ever happened if they had looked a little more like their Norwegian neighbors.

The Hyataka family went to work for my Grandad. They had a truck farm out on the coast someplace, and it was either go to work out in the country away from the coastal area somewhere, or be sent to an Internment Camp…. not much of a choice. The family consisted of two grown brothers and their Mom. No one could pronounce the boys' given names, so they went by Minnie and Nobe. They were good workers and a real nice family. After the War was over they relocated back where they came from.

My Dad and Grandad also had German POWs that worked the fields during the big War. Back in that day and age everyone smoked, and although the government issued them a few cigarettes, it really wasn't an adequate supply for the chain smoker types. One of the German prisoners in particular was always bummin' Dad for a smoke. Of course, knowing the number of cigarettes they were allowed, Dad felt sorry for him and relented. That was a big mistake. It was the same old story every time Dad passed him.

"Got a schmoke? Sure could usse a cigathette."

Dad is a real resourceful type, and wanting to preserve his smokes as well as his generous reputation, devised a plan to get the fellow to stop bummin'. He pulled a long tail hair out of one of the Percheron workhorses and very carefully threaded it down through the tobacco of one of his Lucky Strike cigarettes. Then after clipping off both ends nice and short to avoid detection, he put it in a special place in his pack to keep it separate….. and waited.

Sure enough on their very next meeting…. "Got a cigathette? Sure could usse a schmoke." Dad flipped out the mare tail enhanced, slightly altered "cigathette", gave the guy a light, and went about his work carefully watching for the reaction out of the corner of his eye.

"Tankx," the thankful German responded as he took a big drag off his new "schmoke".

After an extra long draw, the victim inhaled deeply, and then got the strangest look on his face. He pulled the cigarette from his lips, and sat down on a ditch bank, holding it out in front of himself and staring at it as he watched it burned down to a stub…. never taking another drag.

The horsetail enhancement trick was a complete success. The ol' boy must have figured out how to get by with his rationed cigarettes after that, or perhaps he just bummed from someone else, because he didn't bother Dad again.

Wrong brand. For some reason, he just didn't seem to like Lucky Strikes.

126

Chapter Twenty-Six

Dick & Billy Go Duck Huntin'

Dick n' Billy had been hittin' the ball pretty hard a couple of summers ago. They actually had some hay to put up for a change, and with their old rattletrap machinery, and less than perfect mechanical abilities, they had really put in quite a season.

"This fall when we get the work all done, I think we oughta go huntin'," Billy hiccupped one morning while enjoying his favorite illicit liquid breakfast. "A feller can't work all the time."

"A good long rest is what sounds good to me," Dick piped up. "If we ever get all this durn hayin' done, I just want to put my feet up for a while. I'm tired. Trompin' around in the mountains sounds like a lot of work to me."

"Well, how 'bout we go duck huntin'? All you gotta do is put some of those decoy deals on the water an' sit there 'til the ducks show up. Ain't no walkin' to it."

"So what if we shoot one of 'em and it lands in the water? Then what?"

"We'll have to get us one of them trained re-trievin' dogs. They just go right out there an' bring 'em in for you."

That really did sound like a nice way to relax and unwind a little, but Dick pointed out the little hole in the plan. They didn't have any decoys, and they didn't have a re-trievin' dog.

"I was lookin' right here in the back of the paper," Billy pointed as he shuffled through the pile of old papers by his chair. "There's a guy in Massachusetts that raises the best there is…. it say's so right here… and he only wants five hundred bucks for 'em."

"Five Hundred Bucks? Where you gonna get that kind of money?"

"We can sell them two old hoof-rot cows. They oughta bring that much. 'Sides you gotta live a little, Dick."

Dick has always been the more serious of the two, but after a couple more barley sandwiches he was ready to go along with Billy's new idea. It's for sure that neither one of those guys would win an IQ contest. Billy sold the two cows, and ordered the dog. In just two or three weeks, this genuine, high dollar, re-trievin', dog showed up down at the depot with Billy's name on it.

Billy was awful proud of that new dog. He named him Elmer… after the guy he'd gotten him from. He was a happy sort of a pooch, but he was a little bad at eatin' chickens. Elmer always seemed to have feathers stuck on his lips, so the boys had to take a couple of good hayin' days off to build a dog proof chicken pen. Dick got pretty hot about that.

"Dang it Dick, he's a BIRD dog. That's what they're 'sposed to do. It ain't his fault."

128

Billy finally got Dick convinced that all of this pain in the neck was going to be worth it. He was out after supper every night throwin' sticks to practice ol' Elmer up for the real deal. It wouldn't be long now an' the freezer would be plumb full of ducks.

They had a real wet fall that year, and just plain didn't get the hayin' done until almost Thanksgiving. They loaded their shotguns and Elmer and some of those rubber-duck decoy deals in the pickup, and headed up north to the biggest reservoir in the country. Boy, it had sure been cold for the last week or so, and it was especially cold the morning they were ready to go.

One itty-bitty problem. When they got up to Larson's Reservoir, she was froze over. The boys were pretty down in the mouth. They thought that there would surely be open water at Larson's because the reservoir was so big. No such luck.

"I got an idea!" says Billy, trying desperately to save the big expedition from total failure. Let's get two or three sticks of that dynamite that we're savin' to blow out those beaver dams, and blow a hole in the ice. Then we can put our decoys in there and have the only open water for five hundred miles. The ducks will just be beggin' to land here."

Dick wasn't too sure it would work, but that's just what they did. They took the pickup right out on the ice for quite a ways, and then grabbed their shotguns, the decoys and the dynamite and headed out a little further where the ice wouldn't be so thick. Elmer was right there with a big happy grin on his face. The big day was finally here.

"Here... hold my gun while I get a match." Billy instructed. (He was the brains behind this whole operation.) "I don't think we dare go out any further." He scratched a wooden match on the seat of his pants, and lit the two-foot long fuse on the three sticks of explosives in his hand. With a mighty toss that would put a quarterback to shame, he let 'er fly, sending the dynamite sailing out onto the thin ice in the center of the lake.

So far so good, but here is where the plan gets a little sticky. Elmer, remembering all of his after supper re-trievin' lessons, took off after the projectile like he was shot out of a rocket.

"Elmer! Elmer! ELMEEERRR! Git back here!" Elmer didn't hear a thing. He was busy spinning out on the ice. After the dynamite he ran…. as hard as he could go. The explosives hit the ice, and skidded at least another fifty yards, with Elmer in hot pursuit. With a mighty lunge, he grabbed his target, paying absolutely no attention to the sizzling fuse by his chicken-eatin' lips, and headed back for our two heroes.

This is where this story goes from bad to worse. In order to try to keep from gettin' blown to bits, they made a fateful split-second decision. It was either Elmer or them, so they sent a volley of buckshot towards their faithful friend. Elmer was confused. He was far enough away that the buckshot didn't do any mortal damage, but he could see that the boys were really upset about something, so he did what any self-respectin' dog in his position would do. He took his precious cargo in a big wide circle, and hid under the pickup.

Elmer and the four-wheel drive were both buried at sea, and Dick and Billy had twenty miles to walk home. You know, I don't think they've been huntin' since.

"All I can say is it's a durn good thing Lucky wasn't with us."

130

Chapter Twenty-Seven

A Good Son-of-a-Gun

They just don't make 'em like Louie Leonard anymore. Louie was a real horse tradin' fool. He kept this whole neck of the woods in horseflesh for years. I really don't know if he ever made any money at it…. I think maybe he just did it because it was fun. If he ever hurt me on a trade, I dang shore didn't know it. I guess maybe that's one of the signs of a real horse trader.

That was back in the days before anyone had a trailer to haul their horses in, and you almost never saw Louie when he didn't have a horse in the back of his outfit. The stock rack was a permanent fixture on his old pickup, and without exception if anyone would ask about the horse he was haulin', the answer was always the same. "Boy, he's a good one. In fact he's the best Son-of-a-Gun I ever saw."

My Grandad always warned me about tradin' with horse traders. "One of these days you'll wind up with nuthin' but the halter in your hand, wonderin' what happened." That was the advice he gave me the first time I took off with Louie on a horse buyin' trip. Louie Leonard was probably in his fifties someplace, and I was in my early teens. He knew absolutely everybody that raised horses or might accidentally have an extra horse. He also knew everyone within a couple of hundred miles that might be looking to buy or trade one. He just lived and breathed horses.

Louie Leonard
A born Horse-Trader

I was in the market for a horse or two, and just ichin' to know a little more about some of the things that were rolling around in Louie's brain, so I convinced him to take me down on the Fort Belknap Indian Reservation to check out some horses. We made several stops, as most of the folks down that way have got a few horses. Louie knew everybody and where they lived, and everyone knew him. The stop I remember best that day was at George Bradley's. George and his wife were really nice folks and sort of extra kind to a wet-behind-the-ears kid. Sure enough, they just happened to have an extra horse or two, so their son Willie took us out to take a look.

The Reservation has always had its share of good horses. There was still a lot of the old cavalry remount blood in the stock, and the US Cavalry had always used the best

Thoroughbred stallions they could find. I was looking for a colt, and a big stout brown horse colt on a palomino remount mare caught my eye. The mare was eight or ten years old, and only halter broke, so she really didn't interest me, but she was a dang good lookin' horse.

Willie wouldn't part with the colt without selling the mare, too. (He's about half horse trader himself, and knew I really wanted that colt.) Louie, my mentor and equine coach, got me off to the side, and advised that I buy them both. He figured we could resell the mare at an upcoming horse sale, so buy 'em both we did. I forget the exact figure, but we wound up selling the mare for around fifty dollars more than I'd bought the pair for. I weaned the colt, put the fifty bucks in my jeans, and was totally convinced that there wasn't much I didn't know about tradin' horses.

Well, one thing I didn't know became more apparent as time went on. I didn't know much about pickin' out colts. That big stout brown one I'd chosen forgot to quit growin'. I'd picked out a big one all right. His daddy must have been packin' more than a little workhorse blood. My dreams of a rope horse were shattered. Any fool could see this guy would never make the grade.

All was not lost. We called him Drifter, and broke him to work. He was good in harness, and gentle as a kitten, but where he really shined was out of a buckin' chute. He was the perfect size and temperament for a practice horse, and could he ever turn the crank. Ever'body knows if you're going to be a buckin' horse rider, you've got to have practice. We bucked him out for years, both bareback and as a saddle bronc, but with a saddle worked the best.

I finally got to where I could ride him about half the time, but if a fella started gettin' a little too much daylight between himself and the saddle, all you had to do was grab the buck shank with both hands, pull up as hard as you could and hollar, "WHOA". He'd stop, I'd jump off and catch my breath, and then give him a big feed of oats and a little scratch behind the ears. Then we'd just lead him back into the chute to do 'er all over again. He thought buckin' me off was a big game, and about the most fun a horse could ever have.

TJ & his Faithful Pard, Kelly (both are 4 years old)

Louie got us several other horses, too. He showed up with a little Arabian gelding in his pickup one time that was just perfect for TJ, our little four-year-old rug rat. "That's the best Son-of-a-Gun I ever saw," Louie remarked as he unloaded the little palomino. I think maybe he really was. That little gelding was around here until he finally died of old age.

Louie's gone now, and I sure miss him. I really picked up a lot of horse savvy from that ol' boy. You know what? I've got a gelding we got from Ann Davies that I've been ridin' for about ten years, and I'll be durned if he ain't about the "Best Son-of-a-Gun I ever saw".

Chapter Twenty-Eight

Things Ain't That Bad

A couple of the branches of our family tree have their roots south of the Mason-Dixon line in Tennessee. Geographically, that put them on the Confederate side of the Civil War by default, even though none of them had ever owned any slaves, or had any intention of doing so.

There is an account of a young teenaged Rebel soldier who was captured by the Union Army. He was asked if his family owned any slaves, and he answered in the negative.

"Then what are you fighting for?" the officer asked.

"'Cause yer down here meddlin' in our business."

It was a little difficult to take a neutral position during the War Between the States when the Yankees were shootin' at your kinfolk and burning everything in sight. It may be beside the point, but our family didn't have enough money to buy a slave even if they wanted one, so they simply employed the same method of indentured labor as we do nowadays…. work the kids and the ol' lady half to death.

The men folk were off being a part of Jeff Davis' ill-fated war machine, and young Nancy Ann was left home alone, with a new baby and a house full of kids to feed. She was twenty-eight years old in 1861 when she delivered her fourth child.

They didn't have much of anything with real monetary value…. except for the old Stradivarius violin. In all honesty, it probably wasn't an original Stradivarius, but it did have his name in it, and it was the 1860's, so who knows? At any rate, they sure thought it was the real deal, and in order to keep it safe from the thievin' Yankees, Grandad wrapped it in an oilcloth and hid it in a hollow Hickory tree before he marched off to war. The blue coats didn't find it, either…. but they burned the woods down, Hickory tree and all, so I guess it really doesn't matter.

The Union Army took everything of any value, and then set fire to the rest. Nancy Ann had a lot bigger problem on her hands than any missing violin. She gathered her little chicks around her apron, and they quietly huddled in the brush by the creek as the invaders swept though. They thankfully went undetected, and managed to escape any harsh treatment, but quickly realized the stark reality of their situation.

Starvation was a real possibility. There were no neighbors to help. Unfortunately, everyone was in the same boat. The root cellar was emptied, all the livestock had been driven off or butchered on the spot, and the young Mother found herself penniless and without sustenance in hostile occupied enemy territory. She was all alone to care for four kids under the age of six, with her youngest being less than a year old. If our family had a greatest hero contest, Nancy Ann Overcast would probably win hands down.

It's pretty easy for us to complain about how tough we have it, how broke we are, and how bad things look, but it sometimes does us good to hear an old story like this. It helps to keep things in perspective. There are very few folks that have ever been faced with a situation even remotely this desperate. One thing's for sure.... nothing builds your faith like hard times.

When the enemy soldiers had gone, Nancy crept out to survey the damage. It was as bad as she'd feared. There was absolutely nothing left. They say that "Necessity is the Mother of Invention", and Nancy Ann was one ingenious lady. She found an old straight pin; either a hatpin or a sewing needle, bent it into hook, and then with a short piece of string and a willow, they soon had a fishing pole.

The Mother Hen then gathered her tiny frightened chicks again, and assured them that they were going to be fine. "The Lord always answers prayer," she confidently told her sniffling little brood, "and He's going to take care of us." They fastened an angle worm they'd dug from the creek bank onto the crudely bent hook and then prayed the Lord would give them a fish.

"The poor ol' worm had barely hit the water, when the Lord put a big ol' Catfish on that hook," is the story that has been passed down through the family. "The kids prayed every time, and the Lord put on a fish every time." If that wouldn't build a child's faith, what would?

They survived just fine on their Catfish diet until at long last, the ravages of war finally ended. Nancy Ann and the older children were found safe in their little hideaway in the brush, but the harsh ordeal proved too much for the baby, and they buried her shortly before her third birthday. The community's men folk slowly returned, and things gradually got back to normal. "Normal" was abject poverty when compared to our standards.

Don't forget to stop and be thankful for what you have. We all have far more than we really need.

Spread Size

Cowboys 'n women
Got a lot in common
'Specially the ones that's well fed

To avoid a rebuke
From a beknuckled duke
Don't ask 'em the size of their spread

Chapter Twenty-Nine

Lacerated Lessons

*T*hey say the grass always looks greener on the other side of the fence, and I suppose that's true. A lot of folks think that cowboys just ride around in a silver mounted saddle on a perfectly groomed horse and kiss pretty girls as the sun goes down. There doesn't seem to be an awful lot of that going on around here, but I'm sure gonna sign up if I can find the line.

As I look at other lines of work and form opinions based upon what I consider to be intelligent observations, my conclusions are probably just as deluded. Not in the case of fish biologists, though. I think I've got that deal pretty well figured out. Those guys get PAID just to go fishin'. What a deal.

We had one as a next-door neighbor for ten or fifteen years, so I really know what I'm talkin' about. All that guy ever did was go fishin'. Here I am bustin' my buns out in the hay field at 100 degrees, and he drives by pullin' a boat (that somebody else bought), with fishin' poles hanging out of every corner of it. No wonder he always had such a big grin.

In all fairness, those guys probably really do something productive, but it's sure hard to see what it is from the shore. A few years ago there were a couple of those government fish dudes fishin' down on the Fort Peck Reservoir. One of them was an old hand, and the other one a rookie. The old guy was a little on the cranky side, and felt like he'd been demoted to get stuck with the dumb kid that the big brass had assigned to him. The kid was likable enough… just dumb, and the old timer had to explain everything to him at least twice.

This particular day, they were way over on the far side of the lake in one of the inlets with their nets, catching and weighin' fish, and writing all the numbers down in the little tally book that the old guy kept in his shirt pocket.

"Hey, what's that?" the kid questioned.

"It's a Northern Pike," grumbled the boss. "This dummy don't even know a Pike from a Sucker," he thought to himself.

"Not that," the kid answered, his feelings a little hurt that the old guy would think he was that stupid. "THAT!" he said pointing out into the water. There about thirty yards away was something swimming across the inlet.

"I don't know, let's go look," said the ship's captain, as he dropped the net in the bottom of the boat and pulled the rope on the motor. They eased the flat-bottomed boat over closer to the swimming animal to get a little better look.

"Well, I'll be doggoned…. it's a dad blamed bobcat."

Finding a bobcat swimming across an inlet in a lake is really not something you see every day. Cats like water about as much as cowboys do.

"Quick! Hand me that old suitcase we keep some of our gear in." The rookie immediately passed the battered old travel case to the boss, wondering what was coming next, but too intimidated to ask. The old timer dumped the contents out in the bottom of the boat and quick as a wink, scooped up the bobcat from the water and fastened the latches on the scruffy old case.

"What are we gonna do with him?" the kid finally accumulated enough courage to ask.

"Have some fun.... and teach someone a lesson," was the reply, a big grin revealing several assorted snoose stained teeth. It was the first time the rookie had ever seen his boss smile.

They pointed the boat back to the shore, and soon had it loaded on the trailer, and headed towards home, the bobcat riding comfortably in the old valise in the back of the pickup. The old timer chuckled to himself as he hatched the plan, occasionally even including the rookie in what was sure to be the lesson of the century. The sun was just going down as they pulled into Wolf Point to fill up with gas.

"Just set the suitcase there between the gas pumps, and we'll see what happens," the boss commanded. "Somebody's bound to get curious and open the durn thing pretty soon." They pulled their pickup across the street to watch what would happen. Although there was quite a bit of activity at the station, the old suitcase went undisturbed for about fifteen minutes.

It wasn't long, however, until an old 70's something Buick pulled in beside the gas pumps. The fenders were bent, the tires mismatched, the hubcaps missing, and the six or seven occupants were obviously alcoholically enhanced.

"Here we go," grinned the old timer, as one of the drunks grabbed the suitcase and stepped back into the backseat of the car, holding the precious stolen cargo on his lap. The old rattle trap car pulled slowly out of the station, with the fish guys a little disappointed that they hadn't seen them open the suitcase. They turned their pickup in behind the old car and followed it out of town, still hoping to see some action.

They didn't have long to wait. The old car was barely out of the city limits and traveling forty or fifty miles an hour, with the fish boys hot on their tail when the lid blew off. A fella can only imagine the action and reaction that took place in that old car, as some unfortunate soul popped the latch on the suitcase, and released thirty pounds of cooped up, crabby bobcat into the carload of drunks.

The old rattletrap left the road, careening down though the barrow pit, and busted though the barbed wire fence, traveling several feet out into the hay field. It was still rolling along about twenty miles an hour, as all four doors flew open and the scratched and bleeding victims baled out in every direction…. fleeing the wrath of a wet bobcat with blood in this eye.

I'm not totally convinced that being a fish biologist is always so entertaining, but that sure looks like a lot of fun to me.

"I s'pose a job like that 'd be OK, Dick. Long as the boat was big 'nuff to hold all our breakfast."

142

Chapter Thirty

The Taco-Linguini-Tuna Surprise

Alvin and Mary Beth are moving back out to the ranch. Mary Beth really doesn't want to go, but it's either that or stay in town alone, because Alvin's got his mind made up. He never wanted to move off the place anyway, and after what happened last week, he's had it.... back out to the country they go.

Retired really isn't a good word for those folks, because they really haven't quit work, but one of the boys took over the ranch and Mary Beth thought that a house in town would be just the ticket. A ranch lady's social life is a little lacking at times, and she felt it was time to expand their horizons a little.

"Nuthin' doin'!" was Alvin's response to her suggestion. "A feller can't even get any sleep in one of them cities, what with all of the traffic and them sie-reens a goin' all hours of the night. 'Sides there's just too many people fer my way o' thinkin'."

143

"In Cut Bank, Montana?" Mary Beth asked. "Are you sure you don't have that mixed up with Chicago or New York or some place? There can't be more than a couple of thousand people at the most, and I've never even heard a siren.... except for the one time that the grain elevator had that little fire."

They'd spent their entire lives several miles out of town, and May Beth soon had him convinced to at least give it a try. She even agreed they shouldn't buy a house, but just rent one for a while to see how things worked out. This socially starved country gal was completely convinced that if Alvin would just get started drinkin' coffee with the boys downtown that he'd soon fit right in, and they could start looking for a nice little place to buy.

So that's what they did. They rented a little house in a quiet neighborhood.... of course even the noisiest part of town in that little burg would have been a lot quieter than Alvin had figured it would be. There wasn't any traffic, and they very seldom even heard a "sie-reen". Mary Beth got involved in the Lady's Club, and found a couple of old guys that started haulin' Alvin down to the coffee shop. It looked like they might even get the old boy settled in and convinced that town livin' wasn't so bad.

Then the situation started to slide downhill a little. The first thing that went wrong was the Lady's Club got to influencing the cookin'. Alvin is a meat and taters sort of a guy, and all of the strange stuff that the cook got to setting on the table didn't go down with him at all. He was firmly convinced that all casseroles were invented by some sheepherder with only one kettle to cook stuff in. Oh, some of them didn't taste all that bad, but he could never get used to just one pan of stuff settin' in the middle of the table.

"Where's the meat?" he asked politely the first day this happened.

144

"It's in the casserole. Doesn't it smell yummy?"

"Got any taters?"

"They're right here," was the answer as the rurally liberated cook scooped a big helping of her brand new recipe on her hubby's plate. "See?" she said pointing to the middle of the concoction.

Alvin is from the old school. Even though he didn't approve of all of this new-fangled cookin', he had brains enough to keep his mouth shut. Torquin' off the cook is never a good idea.... but then a feller can only take so much. Those city women down at the Lady's Club had succeeded in almost completely pollutin' a perfectly good cook.

It was nearly noon a couple of weeks ago when it really hit the fan. As Alvin pulled his pickup in behind their little rented hacienda in town, the city utility crew had their backhoe out and the alley was all dug up on south of them a house or two. They waved and hollered "Hello" as he walked in for dinner.

Dinner that day was "Taco-Linguini-Tuna Surprise". Little did anyone know exactly how big a surprise it would turn out to be. Mary Beth proudly pulled her new creation from the oven and placed it in middle of the table.

"Sheepherder Stew again," Alvin thought to himself. They went through their little ritual once more, with Alvin politely asking where the meat and potatoes were, and with Mary Beth sweetly indicating that they were contained within her new creation. This was by far the worst thing Alvin had ever tasted, but he ate it like a man, and didn't say a word. He had barely finished his plate when he knew he had a real problem. He could have been getting the flu anyway, who's to say, but the old boy barely made it to the john in time. He quickly made his way to the porcelain throne for a much needed repose.

145

Meanwhile, back in the alley, the city crew was having a dickens of a time. The main sewer line was plugged just above where Alvin's line was connected, and they had tried everything to try and dislodge it. Nothing had worked. Then one of the boys got a bright idea.

"If we just couple a fire hose to the end of the line here, and pour the pressure to it, I think it will push the plug right out."

"Nuthin' else seems to be workin'…. let's give 'er a try."

In all fairness to the crew, it really wasn't all that bad of an idea, and the results were positive, if not a little on the unexpected side. The best that anyone can piece the story together, the boys poured the pressure to the line, and the plug started to move….right past Alvin's sewer connection to an elbow in the line where it stuck again. The line now contained several hundred gallons of water at sixty pounds of pressure, and as water under pressure usually does, began to quite rapidly look for the path of least resistance. That path, unfortunately, was up the line towards Alvin's point of repose.

I'll spare you some of the details. Let me suffice in saying that Alvin wound up splattered against the bathroom door with his jeans down around his ankles, and several hundred gallons of water in the house. It was a real mess.

They say that, "All 's well that ends well", and the results certainly weren't all bad. There's no more casseroles around that camp…. and Alvin started packin' for home as soon as he dried out.

"Now that's disgusting. I think a book
with pictures like that should be
shipped in a plain brown wrapper."

Chapter Thirty-One

Forty Year 'Fess-Up

There are some things that a fella just shouldn't spread around…. take for instance the little story I'm about to tell you. I've been pretty reluctant to share this information for several reasons. Most of them concern the possibility of personal bodily harm befallin' the teller. I'm in hopes that there has been enough water under the bridge by now to sort of dull the anger of the afflicted parties, and they won't seek me out and pound me to a pulp.

The afflicted parties here are Roy and Sally Finley, and the reason I'm so bravely volunteering this information after the passing of forty years or so, is that Sally passed on to her reward several years ago, and I just saw Roy yesterday…. I think I can out-run him. Besides, Sally was the one I was really afraid of.

Roy and Sally and a whole house full of kids lived just up the road from my folks. They were our next-door neighbors, and good ones they were too. Sally was a big hearted, no-nonsense kind of a gal that said what she meant and meant just what she said.

There were some of the Moms in the neighborhood that us kids could get one over on, but Mrs. Finley wasn't one of 'em. You just didn't mess with Sally. She'd kind of taken a shine to me for some reason, and thought I could do no wrong. (Boy, did I have her fooled.) Although I knew very well that I had a special preferential spot in Sally's big heart, even I was smart enough to know that crossin' her wasn't a good idea. It could possibly even prove to be fatal.

Sally & Roy Finley

The Finleys had a mile of county road by the front of their house that doubled as emergency cow pasture. You know how it goes out in the country, there is usually an emergency of some kind brewin' all the time, and so as a result, they generally had cows out on the road. Our family lived on the end of that mile long lane, with a cattle guard to keep the critters apart. It worked out just fine.... most of the time, and Sally was sort of the official cow watcher of that outfit.

150

Now, ever' little boy needs a hero or two, and my little brothers and I had several. The names Jim Shoulders and Casey Tibbs might not mean much to anyone that isn't up on rodeo history, but they were the best back then, and we were determined to be at least that good.... or maybe even better. It doesn't take a rocket scientist to figure out that to get good at anything, you've got to practice, and it also doesn't take a brain surgeon to determine that the constant harassment of gentle domesticated livestock by wild young cowboys with bull ropes and spurs isn't consistent with weight gains and profit.

Dad had threatened us within an inch of our lives if he caught us ridin' his cows one more time. We were pretty sure he meant it, too. He would have been even more upset if he'd caught us ridin' Sally's cows. So far we'd been lucky and nobody was the wiser, and Dad had no idea we could even stoop that low.

Bless my little brothers' hearts, but they have a real evil streak in 'em. I don't recall for sure, but I think this whole deal must have been their idea. The old cattle guard was gettin' kinda full of dirt, and Sally's cows crossed it and got into our place one day. The folks weren't home, so it really didn't take a lot of creativity to get them into the alley behind the buckin' chute we'd rigged up. We bucked them out a couple of times and then opened the gate by the cattle guard and pointed them back up the road towards home.

For some strange reason they didn't wander down to our end of the lane near as often after that, but before long the grass got a little short on the other end and back down they came. The folks were gone again. What luck! We just had 'em all loaded into the alley behind the buckin' chute and ready to go, when our very worst fears were realized.

"Here comes Sally!" yelled one of my little brothers. Both of the little cowards hit the brush, trying desperately

151

to avoid impending death, and left me there to face the music all by myself. I quickly threw the bull rope behind a post, and wisely positioned my body in the line of sight between the window in Sally's car and her cows in the chute across the corral. Drawing my huge four-foot eleven inch frame to its very largest dimension, and pushin' my hat back, I flashed my best smile.

"Hi, Sally. What are you doin' so far from home?"

"I can't find those **&*%$#** cows anyplace. The only thing I can figure is that they must have gone on down the ditch bank into your woods. You seen 'em?"

There were several rules that the folks had drummed into us kids, and one of them was that lyin' was right next to bein' an axe murderer. You always tell the truth…. no matter what. I must confess that I didn't always toe that line as close as I could have as a kid.

I looked her right in the eye, and checking again to make sure I was blockin' her line of sight from the evidence, gave her the only logical answer…. a bald faced lie.

"Nope, I ain't seen 'em," I said lyin' through my teeth. "But I'm sure that's where they are. Don't worry a thing about 'em. I'll ride right down there and run 'em back home for you."

That was one of my closest shaves with death. We made sure we "found" the cows, and never tried that little trick again. The Finley herd coincidentally showed a dramatically increased rate of gain, and the opportunity to see the Overcast name in the Pro Rodeo Hall of Fame went down the drain.

Honesty is always the best policy…. but then if I had always been totally honest, I'd have been dead forty years ago.

Chapter Thirty-Two

Same Old Scenery

Casey Martin and Gumbo Henderson are real buddies. They're about as different as day and night, and all things considered, it's strange that they even like each other. Casey is one of those military-crease-in-his-shirt, starched and pressed Wrangler cowboys, and Gumbo is about the sloppiest piece of humanity that God ever created. If anyone happened to see him without a foot or so of beer belly hangin' out, they'd think they had the wrong guy. He is definitely a s'penders man, not entirely by choice mind you, but because of the size of his over grown paunch, he hasn't worn a belt in over twenty years.

Casey runs a few cows and trains a horse or two up on Windy Ridge, while Gumbo (being true to his name) is a flat land stubble-jumper…. John Deere cap and all. Their common ground just could be that they've neither one found a wife.

Gumbo probably wouldn't be all that particular in his choice of a lady, considering the fact he isn't all that fussy about anything else in his life, but the poor gal would have to be both blind and sniff deficient. Casey on the other hand is sort of a handsome cuss, and I think he even has a few bucks, but he's so dang bashful that unless the gal asked him on a date, AND had him cornered so he couldn't wiggle out of it, chances are pretty good it would never happen.

Well, just last fall Gumbo won some sort of sweepstakes prize. I'll be doggoned if it wasn't an all expense paid trip for two on a big cruise down in the Caribbean. 'Course he knew he wouldn't have any luck tryin' to convince some lady to go with him, so he asked Casey to go along.

"A cruise? Me? I hate water. Besides those boats are probably plumb full of people. Thanks anyway, but you better get someone else to go along. That just don't sound like my cup o' tea." Casey is sort of a loner and greatly prefers four-legged company over that of human-bein's.

"Ah, come on, Pardner," there's prob'ly a lot o' rich wimmin on one o' them deals,' Gumbo pled, his mouth slobberin' at the very thought. "An' it ain't gonna cost ya a dime."

There really was a method to Gumbo's madness. Ol' bashful Casey is a genuine gal magnet, and Gumbo figured that if he just stuck close to him that sooner or later one of the spares that gave up on the cowboy might just take a little interest in him.

A month later they were on a plane to Miami to board the Gypsy Queen. Gumbo was all decked out in his very best Hawaiian shirt, with his red s'penders, a foot or so of his tummy hangin' out, and of course a brand new John Deere cap. Casey still wasn't sure he was glad he'd let his friend talk him into this whole deal. The plane ride was a little bumpy, and as a result, his breakfast was having some difficulty deciding which direction it should go.

It decided to continue down (the breakfast), and somehow the two green country boys managed to figure out which turns to take and which gates to go through. In a couple of days they were somewhere out in the middle of the Caribbean Sea.... havin' the time of their life. Gumbo was really excited about all the girls in their little dinky swimmin' suits, and was making a play for everyone of them that looked remotely unattached. To be honest, he wasn't having much luck in attracting any of their attention, but that really didn't seem to deter him much.

Casey, on the other hand, was doing his bashful best to avoid the single lookin' gals. He wasn't havin' much luck, either. Several of the ladies appeared smitten by this single, handsome Knight of the Plains, and so most of his time was spent trying to give one or the other of them the slip. His ol' faithful Pard was right there by his elbow, trying to salvage anything he could. One of the lines on Gumbo's business card reads like this, "Widows consoled, and Divorcees rehabilitated. Satisfaction guaranteed." Yea, right.

Casey struck up a friendship with one gal, though. Her name was Olga Swendson. Olga was in her mid eighties, and was taking her very first trip off the farm. She was from out in the middle of North Dakota someplace, and had been widowed for about three years or so. A nice old lady she was too, and he felt comfortable around someone that reminded him so much of his Grandma.

One evening just about sundown Casey took a stroll out on the deck, and there was Olga standing right in the bow of the ship taking in the fantastic view. There were little tropical isles everywhere and the sunset was one that you'd never forget. The sea breeze was blowing a little more enthusiastically than it normally did, and Olga had both hands on her straw hat to keep it from blowing away.

Now, this farm gal was from the old school and NEVER went anywhere without wearing a skirt. She just didn't figure it was ladylike to dress any other way. The problem here was that the fresh sea breeze was whippin' up her hemline just as Casey strolled up. Mr. Bashful was embarrassed nearly to tears, and thought ignoring the whole thing was probably the gentlemanly thing to do to. He just looked the other way and began to concentrate intently on the lovely Caribbean scenery.

As the wind gusted still higher, so did Olga's skirt. It was now flapping up around her chin. She seemed totally oblivious, and continued to gaze out across the water in the direction of the sunset, both hands firmly gripping her straw hat. Finally Casey couldn't stand it any longer, and was embarrassed for her.

"Mrs. Swenson, please don't take this the wrong way," he stammered, looking at his boots, "but I think you're dress is blowin' up."

The lady glanced down briefly, never moving her hands from her hat. "Yep, I think you're right." She then returned her gaze to the fantastic vista before her.

"But, Ma'am…. I don't think you understand," Casey stumbled, his gaze never leaving his boots. "I'm afraid you're exposin' yourself!"

Olga looked down again. "Sonny, YOUR'E the one that doesn't understand. I've never seen anything like this sunset before, I'll probably never see one like it again, and this is just a matter of priorities. Anything that anyone happens to see down there is over 85 years old…. and I just bought this hat last week."

Chapter Thirty-Three

Scared and Scarred Bull Bait

Kids come in pretty handy around an outfit like this. The grandkids are starting to take up some of the slack around here now, but for a few years after our kids left home, we got a little short in the indentured servant department. By necessity, country kids learn to do a day's work and hold their own in a lot of different areas and situations. It short…. they're taught how to think.

Dad was kind enough to introduce me to the taste of sweat by the time I was knee high to a grasshopper too, and I think that's one of the reasons I feel confident enough to tie into all the many and varied things I do. Knowing that you're doing a man's work at an early age is a real confidence builder for a young sprout.

While town kids are learning how to squander their youth in front of the boob tube or the enthralling stupidity of a mindless video game, the ones in the country are learning how to run a piece of humungous farm machinery, or

157

to instantly psychoanalyze the mind of a deranged cow while on horseback at a dead run dodging through the brush, in an attempt to determine her intended escape route.

I'd rather have a country kid for back up in just about any situation that required a few brains and resourcefulness than most of the grown up city folks I've met. It's no wonder the out of state corporations want to hire them.... they've had the best training in the world.

We were only blessed with two kids, and they did so much to add to the labor force around here that it wasn't even funny. In retrospect, we probably should have gone to an orphanage in Mexico and picked up a half a dozen more. It would have been a good deal for the kids and us both.

TJ, our oldest, was in the field farming one day when we got some out of state company just before dinner. You should have seen the looks on their faces when this little, less than a hundred pound, nine year old kid successfully maneuvered the dual-tired John Deere and disc between the maze of cars in the yard on his way in for the noon meal.

"That kid's too little to run that big machinery! He's liable to get hurt!" our guest implored.

"That little kid can run anything on the place, and do a pretty good job of it," was my smug reply. I'm convinced that early responsibility has gone a long way in contributing to his success in life, also.

There is one itty-bitty problem with teaching your kids to think, though. Sometimes they think a little too much. Take for instance Karleen, our second born. After her big brother struck out on his own, she was left to fill in the slack. She became my "right hand man" around here, and can dang shore cowboy with the best of 'em. There still isn't anyone I'd rather work cows with.

Karleen milking Ol' Sarah (Age 2)

The problem is she thinks a little too much. She tends to consider silly little things like the possible pain and suffering involved in some of ol' Dad's irresponsible orders, and bein' a girl, she's also a little on the excessively cautious side. Normally that really isn't much of a problem, but it sure was the time we wanted to load an old bull out on the prairie.

This old guy had hoof rot, and the pain involved hadn't helped his disposition much. He really wasn't all that wild, bein' crippled and all, but we had barely gotten him headed up from the creek bottom and pushed out on top out of the brush, when he decided that laying in the shade by the water looked a whole lot better than walking to the corral on a sore foot.

He turned back around, and with all the grace and determination of a chargin' herd of deranged elephants, galloped right back between us. Turning him back was out of the question.... he had his mind made up. Isn't it funny? A

159

critter that can't hardly walk the way you want them to go, can run like crazy back where they came from.

"Can't let him get away," I say to myself, so I built a big loop while in hot pursuit. Whether my catchin' him on the first try was lucky or unlucky is still a matter of rather intense debate around here. This is being written years after the fact, and my little girl "cowboy" still claims to carry emotional scars from the ensuing saga.

"But Daddy! He's gonna KILL me!"

Although I was pretty well mounted, a ton of bull headed downhill through the brush on a dead run is just a little hard to slow down. We finally got him stopped in a big Buffalo Berry patch, and then began the difficult (please read... **IMPOSSIBLE**) task of convincing him that the

160

easiest way to avoid additional pain was to go back up the hill through the brush in the direction of the corral.

I got circled around on his downhill side, but our pleas for his movement from his now nearly choked down position back in the proper direction seemed to fall upon deaf ears. Unfortunately, his disposition seemed to also be deteriorating rather rapidly.

"Hit him with your rope, Karlie."

"I can't, the brush is in the way."

"Then get off and hit him with a stick." She did, to no avail. The old boy wasn't budgin', but by now we had him turned around in the right direction. All he had to do was head up the coulee the way he was pointed. Karlie claims that the following few minutes of her life were among the most traumatic she can recall, and have resulted in deep emotional scarring.

I told you…. she thinks too much.

"Tie your horse up to the brush, and hit him in the face with your stick."

"NO! He'll chase me."

"That's the idea, dumb-dumb. Just head up the coulee so we can get him out on top. Don't worry he can't catch you…. he's tied on to my horse."

"Daddy, he'll kill me!"

"Naw, I doubt it. Surely you can outrun a crippled old bull that's draggin' a horse uphill."

She just flat wouldn't do it. That's the only time I can remember that she disobeyed a direct order. My little girl was completely convinced that doing what she'd been told would result in certain death.

Soooo, while I stayed and held onto our almost captured prize, she rode back and got the pickup and trailer. This resourceful little country kid then unhooked the trailer and backed the pickup down a coulee that would scare a daredevil billy goat, where we tied a towrope on the old boy and drug him up to where we could load him on the flats. Mission accomplished.

You need to teach your kids to think…. but not too much. I still think she could have outrun him.

"Dad blame it, Dick. Too bad there ain't some kids around this outfit. We shore could use a little bull-bait around here once in a while."

Chapter Thirty-Four

Rosie's Rebuke

Rosie worked down at the Co-op when I was a kid. My Dad and Grandad always did a lot of the shoppin' to keep our outfit going at that place, so we got to know him pretty well. I guess his real name was Cloyd Rosenbaum, but Rosie is all anyone ever called him. What a nice fella he was, too. He was a broad shouldered, red faced sort of a guy that walked with a pretty pronounced limp; the lasting result of a horse falling with him as a kid. His gait seemed to get a little worse as he grew older, and his hearing wasn't as good as it could have been either.

He was the guy in charge of the hardware store, and the one that pumped the gas or got the barrel of oil for you from the warehouse across the street from the station if that's what you needed. Rosie was nearly as old has my Grandad, and had worked in that place ever since I could remember.

One July day back in the fifties, he got himself in a real mess. I just happened to be in the right place to hear the entire exchange I'm about to relate, or the poor guy would have probably gone to his grave wondering why that lady from back east had been so rude to him.

Rosie
At His Retirement Party 1970

A big blue Oldsmobile with Illinois plates pulled up beside the gas pump, and as always, Rosie was on the job. His limp got even more pronounced when he was in a hurry, and giving good prompt service was a matter he took very seriously. He hobbled out to the car just as the gentleman doing the driving was getting out.

"Fill 'er up?"

"Sure. Better check the oil, too," the guy said over his shoulder as he headed into the office. "Thanks."

Rosie started the gas pump, then dutifully checked the oil and was just heading around the car, washing all the windows as I happened by. Boy, gas station service sure has slipped, hasn't it? I heard the entire exchange he had with the lady passenger and giggled my way into the station to watch the enfolding drama through the window.

As he approached the passenger side of the vehicle, the lady rolled down the window and said something to Rosie that he didn't quite hear correctly. He smiled and gave her a courteous answer, and hobbled over to the building and began to unroll the air hose that was wrapped around an old tire rim nailed on the wall.

Had I not heard the conversation, the poor guy would have never understood the icy response he received from the lady when he returned. He was standing there, air hose in hand, with a friendly face full of anticipation, as the obviously disgruntled lady rolled up her window, locked the door, and angrily turned her back to the helpful attendant. Totally confused, he re-coiled the air hose and finished the windows, with the clearly indignant lady insolently snarling at him through clenched teeth.

"Wonder what was the matter with her?" he asked (mostly to himself), as he came back into the station and the driver who had finished paying for the gas went out the door.

Now, Rosie was a perfect gentleman, so you can just imagine his horror as I explained the lady's strange behavior through sobs of laughter.

The lady had asked, "Excuse me Sir, but do you have a rest room?"

Now, that seems like a logical enough request, but back in the days before there were vacuum cleaners out near any of the gas pumps and the vehicle floor boards were routinely cleaned with a whisk broom, what Rosie THOUGHT he heard was every bit as logical. Here's what he heard:

"Excuse me Sir, but do you have a whisk broom?"

"No Ma'am we don't," he smiled helpfully. "But don't worry. Just open the door, and I'll blow 'er out with the air compressor."

My Indian Car

I got myself an Indian car
I bought it from a friend
She's only got one gear
And that's the one she's in

The windows are all busted out
And the tailpipe drags the ground
She smokes just like a prairie fire
When I drive her into town

That's the best outfit I ever had
Since I was just a pup
See, I use to drive a cowboy car
Before I traded up

Chapter Thirty-Five

Clarence & The Cow

Clarence had always wanted to go to the Denver Stock show. Opal had never thought it was a good idea, and Clarence always let her have her way. Don't get me wrong here, he definitely wore the pants in the family... the only problem was he ALWAYS wore the ones that Opal told him to.

He couldn't believe his ears when she announced one December evenin' that she had the rodeo tickets and the hotel reservations all made, and they were headed to the big show in Denver right after the first of the year. Actually Opal really didn't do it to please him. It was because she wanted to go herself to get in a little shoppin'. It seems she'd outgrown all her clothes.... again.

Because it isn't politically correct nowadays to say that anyone is fat, I won't even mention the "f" word, but she was one BIG girl.... and gettin' bigger ever' day. As my

167

Grandad used to say, "She's bigger 'n a skinned mule." and it dang sure wasn't a racin' mule either. Opal had a pretty fair frame score too, standing right at six feet in her stockin' feet. That seems a little strange too, as she didn't ever seem to cook much.

Clarence, on the other hand, was kind of a skinny little dried up guy about four inches shorter than his sugar plum. That was more than likely due to a bad shortage of groceries. Because he was a peaceable, mild mannered, slow talkin' sort of a fella, he figured it was a whole lot easier just to sort of go along with the old gal. That approach had spared him a lot of pain through the years.

It's a hard day's drive to Denver from their little spread on Coal Creek, so they left a couple of hours before daylight. By now, Clarence had his sweetie's change of heart and her true motives figured out, but he could care less. He was finally goin' to the Stock Show.

It was almost dark when they finally rolled into Denver, and (of course) Opal was hungry…. again. They had a big steak supper, and then got settled in their hotel, anxious to see the sights. Their schedule was to be in town for the whole week during the big doin's, and they were having quite a time. The rodeos were wonderful, and there were a lot of those "big girl" sort of shops downtown where Opal went hog wild and did her very best to blow her share of the calf check.

It was towards the end of the week when they were in the bull barn that, as Granny used to say, "The cheese got a little bindin'." There was a long parade of combed and curried herd sires of every imaginable breed on display, each with a large poster touting his qualifications and accomplishments. There was progeny carcass data, and rate of gain data, and frame score figures, and maternal trait information, and at least a jillion other pieces of sales pitch baloney that the bull shippers use to tout their particular bloodlines to the prospective customers.

168

With her dominant and overbearing nature, Opal began to compare poor little Clarence to the bulls as they made their way through the barn. Every time they would approach a sort of young, smallish dairy breed bull, she'd make a wise remark about his size, and then look askance at her hubby out of the corner of her eye.

Clarence didn't even answer her taunts. He'd just pull his hat down, mumble something unintelligible under his breath, and sink a little lower into his Tony Llamas. But the mean spirited woman just wouldn't let it die. She continued to mock him, and the further they went down the row of bulls, the worse the situation became.

As they approached the far end of the barn, they came upon several massive sires that had been used extensively in a national AI program. One huge Angus bull in particular really stood out from the rest, weighing in at nearly three thousand pounds, he fairly dwarfed the others, and his records showed that he had sired thousands of calves.

"Holy cow, Clarence. Get a load of that," Opal said as she pointed a fat dominant finger at the chart on the wall. "We need to find out what they're feedin' him. A ration like that might just help your puny little hide…. in more ways than one," she laughed, nearly knocking him down with a slap on the shoulder.

A fella can only take so much, and this time Clarence reached way down inside his poor old hen-pecked soul for an answer. "I don't know how he got that done or what they're feedin' him, but I know one thing for dang sure. I'll bet my bottom dollar he didn't spend all of his time last year on short grass with the same old swing bagged, over finished dry cow."

"Over finished dry cow, my foot! As if a gal comin' up dry is always her fault. It takes two to tango, ya know."

Chapter Thirty-Six

Gift Wrapped Left-Overs

*D*ick and Billy are those two bachelor yay-hoos that grub out a livin' doing about anything they can to turn a buck. They run some cows down on the south slope on about the poorest chunk of real estate you ever saw. Their place is mostly just alkali and grease wood flats. Some guys say they think God plumb forgot about that country when he was layin' the world out.

Hard times really don't seem to bother those guys much, though. They're sort of like those old cows you see that haven't known anything but short grass and hard winters with no hay…. they've got a permanent hump in their back. I think it must be genetic. They just get built that way after a while, and don't really know the difference. The poor old girls have never known anything but hard times, and think the whole rest of the world is in the same shape.

Dick and Billy have seen their share of tough times too, and that, coupled with their over-indulgence in copious quantities of illicit liquids (that would kill someone of lesser constitution), and the normal wear and tear of life out on the plains have all taken their toll. Just like those old cows on short grass, they've both got a permanent hump in their back and a hungry look in their eye most of the time. They pro'bly look at least twenty years older than they really are.

The boys try to make a few bucks tradin' horses, and usually have a few young ones around that need some miles on them. So with a barn full of colts that needed riding, they saddled up a couple of big stout ones for a long circle right after Thanksgiving a few years ago. We had a nice long fall that year, and the temperature was probably in the forties someplace.

They rode clear over on the far side of the ridge, and about the middle of the afternoon ran into one of the Richarson brothers over there tying up a little fence. It was a pretty good day for a ride, or maybe to fix some fence, but when Lenny Richardson pulled the bottle of hooch out from behind the seat of his pickup…. it turned into a PERFECT day for visitin'.

It was Dick and Billy's favorite brand, too…. somebody else's. One thing led to another, and they chewed the fat for quite a while. They had been travelin' partners years ago when they had all chased the rodeos together, and there was quite a bit of catchin' up to do.

Everybody in that part of the country has really taken a shine to those two old broken down cowboys, even if they do tend to drink a little too much. After all, either one of 'em would give you the shirt right off his back, and they're always there to lend a hand when you need it. As the afternoon wore on and the sun began to set, Lenny suggested that the boys just ride on over to his place for supper.

172

"I don't know what the little woman has on the stove…. might just be leftovers again, but I'm sure she'll rustle us up somethin'. Besides, I've got a Christmas present for you guys, and it'll save me havin' to bring it over. I got it all wrapped up and ever'thing."

If there's one thing that bachelors the world over have in common, it's the propensity to never turn down a free meal, and Lenny Richardson's wife has a reputation of being as good a cook as there is out that way.

"Shore…. won't hurt to ride on home after dark," Billy answered as he took the last pull from the bottle of hooch. They threw the fencing material and tools back in Lenny's outfit and the boys mounted their horses and followed the old rattle trap pickup down off the ridge to the Richardson outfit.

"Sure is nice of him to ask us fer supper," Dick remarked to his partner. "Leftovers sounds a whole lot better 'n yer cookin' to me."

"Whatdaya mean my cookin? I cooked last night," came the slurred reply in the gathering darkness. "It's YER turn."

"Hoo-wee!" Billy went on, his whisky brain suddenly turned from chore arguments to thoughts of a hot meal. "Free supper and a wrapped up Christmas present… what a deal! Leftovers sound purty good to me, too. She's been a long time since breakfast."

There was a little light on in the kitchen…. but not much of one…. as the boys tied their horses to the tailgate of the old pickup and the trio headed up the walk to the house. Little did the fellas know that Mrs. Richardson had chosen this very evening to surprise her husband with a special candlelight supper complete with some high dollar dinner wine and a unique twist or two. She had been reading in one of those racy women's magazines about ways that a lady can perk up her overworked old husband and put a little romantic spark back into their marriage, and she had devised a very special surprise for him.

174

The three boys walked silently up to the front door. They really weren't being quiet on purpose, but after all they'd been visitin' for three or four hours, and there just wasn't much left to say. Dick's mind was on the warm supper that was sure to hit the spot, leftovers or not, and all Billy could think about was the wrapped Christmas gift that Lenny had mentioned. "It's probably a bottle," he was thinkin' to himself as he licked his lips.

Lenny held the door for the two guests in the standard show of Western hospitality, and the two bachelors pulled off their hats and stepped into the kitchen. It's really hard to say who was the most surprised.

There (in all her glory) stood Mrs. Richardson.... all perfumed up and decked out just like the romance enhancin' expert had advised.... dressed in nuthin' but some of that see-through kitchen wrap stuff you use to cover up dishes in the refrigerator. Neighborhood rumor has it that her wardrobe also included two or three strategically placed Christmas bows.

She gasped, and the boys' lower jaws hit the floor. They just stood there with their hats in their hands, lookin' two-eyed; searching for something to say.

"Leftovers again!?!?" Dick stammered.

"Gift wrapped!?!?" Billy gasped.

"I'm a thinkin' maybe we could use a cook around here too, Dick. Mrs. Richardson bakes a mean loaf o' bread, and she's dang shore easier to look at than you are. 'Specially the way she's dressed that day. 'Course I'll keep on rustlin' up breakfast just like before."

Chapter Thirty-Seven

Pickin' A Race Horse

*T*here's a lot a fella can learn from old timers. I really hope that I'm not in that category with both feet yet, but I ain't exactly brand new any more so if you'll just pay a little attention, I'll pass on a secret that I pried out of an old timer once. An ol' boy told me one time that a man needed to be like a good horse… "Just keep your mouth shut and pay attention…. you might learn something."

This little learnin' experience of mine took place back in the early sixties. Down the river from us fifteen miles or so, close to where Snake Creek hits the Milk River, live a couple of cowboys that could teach any young buckaroo something if they just had the brains to listen. I'm not sure if they're old enough to be called "old timers", but Bruce and Doris Johnson have been good hands with horses ever since I can remember. Now don't go gettin' your feathers all ruffled up about me callin' Doris a cowboy... just 'cause she happens to be a lady. A real "cowboy" doesn't have anything to do with gender. It's all about mind set and attitude.... guts and ability.

As I travel all over the country at singin' cowboy deals, real cowboys like the Johnsons are a little on the scarce side. The way some of those dudes come all gussied up to the doin's is enough to make a fella laugh. They show up with their pants all jammed down in the tops of their 24" stove pipe boots and with silver jingly bob spurs that have never even seen a horse hangin' on the heels.

They've always got their Tom Mix hats and wild rags big enough to make a sail for the Mayflower all very properly color-coordinated. Not that a real hand might not dress like that, but there sure is a whale of a difference. I'm certain they think they're real cowboys, but one of the first things you have to figure out is which end of a cow the hay goes in, and they ain't got a clue. They couldn't even GET ON that ol' pony that Doris used to ride to jingle in the milk cow.... much less stay on.... and then get the cow in.

I like to visit with Bruce and Doris, I always have, but back in the front part of the sixties I used to hang around down there a lot. Just for the record, it had absolutely nothin' to do with the fact that their ranch house was also home to two of the best lookin' gals on the Milk River.... one a daughter, the other a niece.

Contrary to the belief in some circles, it is also just a coincidence that I didn't visit them near as often after the two beauties in question began to throw rocks at my pickup every time I got within range. Sorry I digressed from the lesson here, but we have to keep the record straight, and I need to make perfectly clear that my sole interest in visiting down that direction was to learn all I could about bein' a cowboy. (Cowboys don't go to hell fer lyin', do they?)

There used to be saddle horse races at a lot of the County Fairs in years past, and I happened to run into Bruce at the Great Northern Stampede in Havre. "Here's my chance," I thought to myself. "Bruce has forgotten more about horses than I know… I'll see if I can pick his brain a little."

Saddle horse races are a lot of fun. They're not so formal as those real jockey kind of races with the starting gates and all, and boy some of those nags could run. I sidled over close to Bruce as he was casting a discerning eye on the fresh crop of horses loping back and forth on the track.

"Waddaya think about that sorrel?" I questioned, trying to act like I probably knew as much as he did.

"That's a good lookin' horse… but I don't think he can win," Bruce answered quietly. Boy I was frustrated, but just kept prying for the information it seemed to me he was intentionally holding back.

"Look at that hind quarter on that bay," I stated as I alternately studied the horses parading on the track and Bruce's poker face. Actually, it was really more of a question than any kind of statement about the pony's conformation.

"Yea, I'm sure he can run," my mentor answered. His voice sort of trailed off, and then after what seemed like ten minutes, he finally continued, "I'm not much of a bettin' man, but if I was, I'd put my money on that brown mare."

As they made the final trip past us back to the starting line, I studied every part of that brown mare as she slowly cantered by. Soon the race was underway, and as they thundered past us, the brown mare was neck in neck with the sorrel and the bay, but by the end of the race, she was a comfortable three lengths in the lead.

"This old buzzard really knows his stuff," I thought to myself.

Every race after that our ritual was the same. I would comment on one horse and then the other with Bruce just silently and intently watching them. His answer was nearly always the same. "I'm not a bettin' man, but if I was I'd put my money on...." and then he'd make his pick, and I'd try desperately to figure out what he was looking at. His horse didn't always win, but they were always up close to the front of the pack, and I'll be doggoned if I could figure out how he was doing his pickin'. Finally, there were only a couple of races left, and again I got the same answer.

"I'm not a bettin' man, but if I was I'd put my money on that sorrel."

My frustration meter was pegged out by now, and I just couldn't stand it any longer, so I let down my cowboy pride enough to just flat out ASK him what he could see that I couldn't.

"Is it the length of the legs, the way the neck is set into the shoulders, the slope of the hind quarters, the length of the pasterns... what in the world are you looking at?" I inquired with an inquisitive frustration he probably found amusing.

"It's the Indian kid."

"Huh?"

"The rider.... when the horses all look pretty good, if I was a bettin' man, I'd put my money on one of the Indian kids. Chances are pretty good they'll be right in there at the lead. Those Indian boys are dang hard to beat."

Chapter Thirty-Eight

The Volkswagen Cowboy

*B*owman is nestled in the sure-nuff cowboy country of southwestern North Dakota. If a fella was to draw a circle around that fair little city with about a hundred and fifty mile radius, you'd probably have just drawn a line around the highest concentration of good cowboys in the entire world.

Casey Tibbs the famous bronc stomper would more than likely head the pack, based simply on all his World Championship buckles, but then there's the famous bulldoggin' town of Buffalo, South Dakota, just down the road a few miles, and of course the big annual Miles City, Montana Buckin' Horse Sale. All the wild and wooly boys around that old cow town would make it in the circle, too.

The Penfield's ran the auction barn in Bowman for many years, and also had an annual buckin' horse auction that they ran continuously there for 18 years. As a matter of fact, it was the second oldest event of its kind, with only Miles City having run longer.

Bob Penfield is the third generation involved in the auction business there, following in the big boots that his Dad and Grandad have left him. Bob had a couple of good teachers. He grew up with both the ability of a good cowboy, and the savvy of a horse trader. He can think on his feet. That must be why he came up with that crazy sounding plan to use a Volkswagen to capture an old renegade stud horse.

The horse belonged to Ed Gardner from down in the Harding County, South Dakota country. The Gardner's had a string of horses with quite a little draft blood in them, and Bob had gotten the horses bought for their annual buckin' horse sale. They were just what he was looking for.... the perfect size and age to make good buckin' horses. They'd never had a hand on them, with studs all the way up to five or six years old.

I don't know the exact details of their deal, but if I remember right, Bob had bought them by the head with the condition that he had to "Take 'em all."

Well, "takin' 'em all" included the renegade stud I mentioned earlier. He was a bay horse about six years old. He was born in that pasture and had never been out of it. When the other horses were gathered out of that particular field every year, the devious old renegade would head for the brush.

In a country containin' that many cowboys, a horse that nobody can seem to corral is quite a challenge, and a lot of dang good hands had taken a crack at him. A man had to be pretty well mounted to even run up on him, but by the time he got within roping distance, the old stud would turn, lay his ears back, bare his teeth and come at you with his mouth open. Any horse or cowboy with a lick of sense quickly became the chase-ee.

They'd tried everything. They'd tried mare bait, but ol' bay was too wise for that. It didn't work. One of Ed's hired men had made a run at him with a new four-wheel drive pickup, but the country was pretty rough, and he'd left the front end of it four feet down in a washout. It seemed even trying to corral that horse was useless, and everyone had all but given up.

Bob talked to the local Veterinarian about using a tranquilizer gun, and had gotten the advice that he could sure use his gun, but he didn't think his tranquilizer was powerful enough to get the job done. That's when the Volkswagen Cowboy came up with the plan to use Black Leaf 40.

I'm not really sure where he got that idea. Black Leaf 40 was an old nicotine based chemical that was used at the time to fumigate green houses, and to spray the mites off of the roosts in your chicken coop. The recipe isn't exactly common knowledge, so Bob tested his experimental concoction on a few killer horses down at the stockyards. He chose horses that weighed in at around 1500 pounds, to be the size of the renegade, cutting the powerful substance with water and alcohol until he thought he had his mixture about right.

"Bob, part of the deal is I want that bay horse out of that pasture," Ed reminded.

"I know. I think we can get him. We've got a tranquilizer gun and a Volkswagen."

That must have sounded like a hair-brained plan to Mr. Gardner, but he was game for just about anything. Nothing else had worked.

"Here. Take my 30-30," Ed said skeptically as he handed over his old Winchester. "I want that stud horse out of that pasture one way or the other. Just bring me the ears if your plan doesn't work. Good luck."

Bob had recruited Gib Wood and Albert Chapman to give him a hand, and like you'd expect of a gang of cowboys, they just had to try running him out of the field with horses first. After all, what a feather those boys would have had in their hat if they'd accomplished the task where so many other good hands had failed. Unfortunately, it didn't work for them either.

Bob Penfield, The Volkswagen Cowboy
At the Guthrie, Oklahoma Ranch Rodeo Finals
Their team won second place in the Wild Cow Milking.
Bob was 67. (If they would have let him use his
Volkswagen, they probably would have won.)

The old Volkswagen had a sun roof, so with Gib Wood stickin' out the top as his gunner, Bob headed for the stud. They somehow managed to stay out of the washouts, and ran the ol' boy around the pasture for a couple of hours, shootin' him in the rear end with the tranquilizers. It wasn't long until they were out of dope, and the stud was still on his feet.

184

They did manage to make him good and drunk. The ol' boy would stand sort of spraddle legged and stare at them with bleary eyes filled with contempt until they'd try to move in a little closer, and then away he'd go again, stumbling off in a drunken trot, eventually gaining the mental faculties to get into a staggering lope.

With the pasture being so rough, there were very few spots to take a good run at him, but they eventually managed to get him into the middle of a ten acre flat and let him stand there in a stupor while they tied two ropes together. The boys then tied one end to the bumper of a half ton pickup, and with Albert Chapman in the back with the loop in his hand, away they went again.

"When I yell, that means I got 'im caught. Just punch the gas on this outfit and go on by."

After a try or two, Bob heard a yell, and he kicked the old pickup in the rear end. Around the stud horse they flew. When Mr. Renegade hit the end of the rope there was a fairly sudden stop for all the parties involved. Albert baled out and in a few minutes the boys had him hogtied and in the trailer.

By sundown the Volkswagen Cowboy and his trusty sidekicks had the heretofore "uncorralable renegade" safely captured in Gardner's big round pen. The old pony was a little hung over and pretty well steamed up from being galloped around for most of the afternoon, but all in all, none the worse for wear.

I think this little story exemplifies a couple points well worth pondering:

1. Never underestimate the wily resourcefulness of the great American horse trader.

2. But probably an even more important lesson: ....NEVER, EVER, buy a second hand car with a sun roof from a cowboy. (Especially if there's sagebrush danglin' from the bumper.) 🔺

"'Scuse me. Don't go away..... I'll be right back.
I think I've got a phone call."

Chapter Thirty-Nine

Deep Thinkin' Country Boys

*C*ountry boys tend to make some of the best soldiers. It isn't any coincidence that during World War II, the First Special Forces unit was trained and headquartered in Fort Harrison near Helena, Montana. It also wasn't by accident that it was comprised largely of country boys who had recently spent their formidable teenage years trying their level best to help their families survive the drought and financial challenges of the Great Depression. They were a tough bunch of dudes.

When exposed to the harsh rigorous physical training of boot camp, those guys probably actually lost a little of their muscle tone. Young men in their prime that are accustomed to hard manual labor from sun to sun tend to get a little on the wirey order.

There is one problem with country boys and the military, though. Their life of self sufficiency tends to make them think for themselves. The US Army views that particular trait as an affliction rather than an asset. Oh, it isn't that that they don't know how to take orders or that they refuse to treat their superiors with respect, it's just that they don't have an inclination to leave their brains at home when they enlist.

I was in the Montana National Guard back in the 60's, and got a first hand view of how country boys operate. We were an armored unit, and were trained in M48 tanks. The country boys soon learned that when they were sent out to fire the 90mm main gun, that there was a way to get back out of the field and back into town a little more quickly.

The superiors wanted to spend all day long on the firing range, "practicing", but the country boys for some reason thought that the poker game back at the barracks was something that was fairly important. They couldn't go back to town until:

A. They shot up all the ammunition.
B. The targets were all blown down. *or*

Why spend all day long out there shooting up that valuable ammunition? "Just aim for the edges and blow the targets down, boys and we can go back to town."

"The edges" were the two by six's that were on each side of the white cloth targets. The targets themselves were about six feet square and were stationed at various ranges. Some were stationary, and some were moving. You just have to hit the boards on the edge of the target, and she falls down. A six inch target isn't all that big, but much to the chagrin of the "by the book" officers in charge, those boys knocked 'em down ever' time. But then, I guess if you can hit a six inch moving target at 1500 meters maybe you don't need that much practice.

"Just aim for the edges, boys. When we knock 'em all down we can go back to town."

Dick Bressler was a staff sergeant, and the tank commander on a war games mission I was on in the desert south of Boise one summer. I'm not sure if Dick had an official drinkin' problem or not, but he sure did like the stuff. Bein' one of those country boy thinker types I was telling you about, he discovered that he could take a little nip along on this "silly little game", and keep it fairly safe from probing eyes by sliding the breach open on the 90mm main gun and slipping his fifth of booze in there. After all, a bottle of booze is just a little smaller that 90mm, so in Dick's eyes the hiding place was almost perfect. He was so proud of himself that he took a little drink right after breakfast.

Dick really knew about military tactics and strategy, but just couldn't see any reason to take a game too seriously. I was the gunner on this particular mission where we were to be an aggressor in the war games. It was near

189

the close of our summer training period, and everyone but us got to go back to town. None of the crew was too happy about being chosen, but someone had to do it, so we just made the best of it. We were to help test the readiness of a unit of infantry and armor several miles south in the desert near the Snake River. Dick had another little snifter off his stash.

The tank gunner is the second in command, and the only guy on one of those machines that can't stick his head out and see where he's going, so I pulled rank on the driver, and made him ride down where he couldn't see, and I took over the driving job. The former driver got back in the gunner's chair, and Dick took another little swig.

They furnished us with a map of where we were to go, so Sergeant Dick had one for the road and away we went. We took a dirt road straight south for several miles, turned at a large cone shaped mountain, and went straight east for several more miles. Dick had a drink to celebrate. We then came to another large cone shaped old volcanic mountain, and turned straight south again for several more miles.

Dick had another little nip.

We got to our destination just before dark, and took our ordered position. We were to do a war game ambush on a night convoy coming by. It was sort of fun actually, as we were all loaded up with blank rounds for the machine guns. Dick had another blast or two from his bottle.

We did our little job, and were scheduled to head back into the base at daylight. Dick would have celebrated the sun coming up, but unfortunately by now his stash had gone dry. I turned the tank north up the road towards town, which was probably forty or fifty miles away, and seeing those two conical shaped mountains looming on the horizon in that vast sea of desert, got a brilliant idea.

"Sergeant Bressler," I inquired over our intercom radio to my commander, "let's cut across. If we just head northwest right between those two mountains, and keep on that heading we'll hit the road again about ten miles south of town. It'll save us two or three hours of drivin' time. Whaddaya say?"

Sargent Dick Bressler
163rd Armored Cavalry
"A deep thinkin' country boy and
a dang good guy."

I got an immediate answer. "Sshsmifix. Berful mekel gibelixxsson."

I know, I know…. I couldn't understand it either, but because it was such a good idea I just naturally assumed that he meant OK, so I headed the fifty tons of armor angling off across the desert as fast as she'd go. We had sand and dust fifty feet in the air behind us as I dropped the hammer and to town we went. The calculations were brilliant, if I must say so myself, and we hit the road again a few miles south of town just like I'd figured we would.

When we arrived the entire base was in an uproar. It seems that the most of the day's operations had been interrupted. Country boys are thinkers, remember? They think on their feet, and find ways to save time and money, right? At least they do if they have all the facts to make the right decisions.

"What's goin' on?" I hollered at a sergeant, seeing the base in a turmoil.

"They had to shut six artillery ranges down. Some idiot in a tank drove right across 'em, and screwed up the whole day. They're out there lookin' for the tank now. Heaven help those guys if they catch up with 'em."

Of course, we hadn't seen a thing. So much for thinkin' for yourself and savin' the government a little money.

Chapter Forty

Big Sandy BS

*H*oly cow, but the wind can blow in this country. A guy from Cut Bank, Montana (perhaps the wind capital of the world) told me that actually, the wind really didn't blow up that way. "It's just that Idaho blows and North Dakota sucks, and we just happen to be right smack dab in between 'em." Maybe that's it.

I happened to run into Keith Edwards the other day, and of course I mentioned how bad the wind had been the last few days. "Ah, this really ain't nothin'. You should o' been along with me 'n Charlie Dogsleep and what's-his-name back in '36."

I made the fatal mistake of askin' one little question, "Really?" and it took him an hour or so to tell me this little story.

Keith is quite a historian from down around that Big Sandy country and is one of those old-timers that remembers everything all the way back to the Civil War. It doesn't even make a lick of difference whether it ever really happened or not.... he can remember it perfectly either way. I'll try my best to relate what he told me, and if a few of the facts sound like they're jumbled up a little, it's because the jumblin' up is in between Keith's ears. Here goes:

1936 must have been quite a year. He told me it was one of the hottest and driest that anyone had ever seen. It was so bad that the rattlesnakes got to climbin' the fenceposts just to try to get a breath of fresh air, but the very worst part of all was the hot wind that blew out of the southwest.

He and Charlie Dogsleep and "What's-his-name" were trailing a little bunch of cows across the open range west of Lonesome Lake when this little incident occurred. I've yet to take the time to check it out, but he claims that Lonesome Lake is as dry as yesterday's biscuits, and has been ever since anyone can remember, but for some reason the government folks still color it blue on the highway map. Keith thinks that maybe the crazy birdwatcher folks have something to do with that.... "Tryin' to fool the ducks."

Well, right smack dab in the middle of that old dry lake bed is where the big wind caught them. They were riding those old high backed saddles, and the wind caught the cantles of those rigs just like a weather vane. It blew their horses around at a right angle and, of course, blew the boys off on the ground. There they were afoot. Gettin' blew out of the saddle must have been something that happened fairly regularly back in those days, as he really didn't make a big deal out of it.

One of the cows was a big skinny blue roan that they called Outie. Times were tough back then, and there were lots of scrub bulls around. Nobody had the money to buy a good one, and when one those scrubs set up housekeepin' with one of the homesteader's milk cows, you got something that looked like Outie. That's where she'd come from. She was uuuuugly, and had come by her name honestly. The durn thing was always out. She was one of those old fence crawlin' son-of-a-guns that thought the grass must be greener on the other side of the fence, so out she'd go.

This particular year, the old girl had a little bitty calf that the boys had nicknamed Bootie. He was just a little nubbin' of a guy, and had to stand on a rock just to get a suck. Nobody knows if the wind had blown him in that badger hole, or if he'd just fallen into it, but all of a sudden Bootie was lost, and Outie couldn't find him anywhere. Now, there's not anything more upsettin' to a Mama of any kind than a lost baby, and she was running around wringin' her tail and bawling her face off looking for him.

The boys were just layin' there on the ground holding on to the sagebrush to try to keep from blowing plumb away, and they saw exactly what happened next. Outie turned around into the wind and opened up that big blue roan mouth of hers to let out a beller, and I'll be doggoned if a big gust didn't go right down her throat and blowed her plum inside out.

Charlie was fairly close to her when it happened, and Keith says that he was a good pard to ride with. "A fella could always count on Charlie in a pinch." He was one of those guys that always seemed to be prepared and in the right place at the right time. "He pulled a piggin' string out of his back pocket and reached right down her craw. Charlie managed to get a half hitch on her tail, but try as he may, he could only get her pulled about halfway back in shape."

Apparently she must have stretched something when she went inside out, because even with all three of them pulling on the piggin' string, they couldn't ever get her completely back like she was before. "She was always a little scrambled after that, and we were constantly tryin' to figure out which end to feed."

By George, I believe Keith's right. I never have seen a wind as bad as that one back in '36. Keith Edwards is a real storehouse of completely useless information, and the folks around Big Sandy are so grateful for all of the work he's done in the Museum to help preserve the history of the area that they've even considered erecting a bronze statue of him there on the grounds.

Unfortunately, it looks like that's going to cost way too much money, so a couple of the ol' boys up that way have talked to a taxidermist. They figure that when Keith crosses over the Great Divide that maybe they could save a chunk of change if they just have him stuffed. Not only is it a lot cheaper than a statue, but if they prop him up in a corner of the museum, they won't have to worry about the pigeons.

It looks like the price is going to be really reasonable, too. The taxidermy man said that anyone that full of BS wouldn't take much stuffin'.

Chapter Forty-One

My Little Barnyard Barbie

*T*here sure are a lot of little girls hangin' around our place, and modesty is something that doesn't seem to come very naturally to kids for some reason. Last week we had three grandkids.... two girls and a boy, buck naked swimmin' in the puddle out in front of the tractor.

They didn't even seem to mind that their swimming hole was created by the gunk that I'd flushed from the radiator that morning. In the event that ever happens at your house, don't panic. I have a little good news for you. What ever is in that radiator flush stuff doesn't seem to hurt kids a bit. Didn't even turn 'em red. (I nearly forgot to mention that the boy of the bunch thought the puddle needed a little more water, so.... never mind.)

Of course with this extra sprinkling of little girls also comes the varied assortment of scantily clothed or (more often) buck naked Barbie Dolls. Now I sure don't claim to be a Barbie Doll expert, but I did notice something the other day that got me to thinkin'. These dolls come in just about every character and for nearly every occasion that you can possibly imagine. They've got them for all the sports and fairytales and ethnic groups; you name it, they've got it, and their wardrobes are just as varied as the characters. They've got one thing in common.... when they're buck naked, it's a little hard to tell which one's which.

That got me to thinkin' about a new source of cash flow. I figure that I can both create a little income for this strugglin' outfit, and give the country girls of the West a bit of a boost in the social standing department at the same time. You see, most of the grown up girls that I travel with would look just as good as their city cousins in some of those skimpy little outfits, but Carhartts and snowboots just aren't all that conducive to the flattery of the feminine form. So, as a result, country girls are more often than not relegated to the unkempt and frumpy category by the uneducated and uninformed masses. Now, that's just not fair. Hence, my latest creation... The Barnyard Barbie.

Now, Carhartt bibs or coveralls aren't going to be mandatory, but they will be standard equipment on the basic model. That will, of course, just be the very outer layer. In my quest for a realistic depiction of rural femininity, I've actually done some very extensive research.

Beneath the lovely brown duck, barnyard splattered outer garment (complete with balling gun, scour pills, 10cc plastic syringe, 100cc bottle of injectable antibiotic, a handful of wooden matches, a pocket knife, and a tube of hot pink lipstick (for just a little touch of glamour), will lie several inner layers of wool, flannel and denim that may mixed and matched to taste. Lest I forget, the entire ensemble will also include the very finest union suit long johns and skimpy flour sack lingerie. (Eat your heart out

Victoria's Secret) I'm tellin' you, this new Barnyard Barbie is going to be every little girl's dream. What a wonderful role model she can be.

The girls of the West will finally get their due, and before long I can envision one of them gracing the cover of Comso Magazine with a seductive hot pink lipsticked smile, and one hand provocatively resting on a shapely Carhartted hip. I've gotten a look like that in the calvin' shed a time or two... but then that's another story.

Here's Dawn, my own personal Barnyard Barbie, feedin' chickens at 50 below zero.

Country girls aren't all about glamour, either. We were pregnancy testin' some cows a few years ago, and the lady of our house insisted that she was the one that was going to run them up the chute. Actually, I think she got the job by default, because she's too short to reach the squeeze chute handle without standin' on a five gallon bucket, and even when she can manage to get a hold of it, her whoppin' 95 pounds of muscle mass is somehow just a little on the deficient side.

All was going well until she came to one of the old pets. There was a big, fat, gentle, old Hereford cow that probably weighed 1400 pounds or so, and she really didn't feel like going up the chute. She had all four feet planted and wasn't going anywhere. Little did that old cow know that she'd more than met her match. The Vet seemed truly amazed as he turned his gaze back down the alley to ponder the ongoing scene of the beauty vs. the beast.

My lovely little bride had one shoulder straining against the rear end of the brute, with the old cow's tail twisted in a number nine up by her right ear. Previously digested grass and hay covered the cheek of my little darling's face as she pressed it firmly against the part of the cow from whence the digested material was still being ejected. Words of the most vile and unladylike nature were flowing freely from her pretty little lips.

He turned to me and said, "You know, pound for pound I think that's the meanest woman on the face of this earth."

"And he's right, too! My tail's
never been the same since."

200

Chapter Forty-Two

Gentle As A Dead Pig

The sun was just beginning to set. Dick and Billy were perched out on the porch enjoying a warm evening last spring, when they heard the distinct rattle of a horse trailer coming over the hill.

"Wonder who that could be?" Dick belched as he reached for another barley sandwich. (He'd been on the wagon for a while, but because he and Billy split the groceries 50-50, he had to start drinkin' again just to get his money's worth.)

"I'll be doggoned if 'n it don't look like ol' Slick Jacobson's outfit," Billy slurred in reply as the pickup pulled in the yard. Slick was a horse trader deluxe, and always seemed to have some old plug in his trailer that was lookin' for a home. Ever' once in a while he accidentally came up with a dandy.

Sure enough, it was Slick alright.

"Howdy, boys," Slick called as he slammed the pickup door. "Nice evenin' ain't it?"

"Slick…. I thought that was you. I heard you was down to Arizona monkeyin' around on the racetrack," Billy hollered. "Come on over an' have somethin' to wet yer whistle." Dick dug out a cold one for their visitor.

"I jus' got back…. ran across the best lookin' geldin' I seen in a long time down there. I drug him back up this way an' I thought I'd give you boys the first chance at 'im. I think he's the best son-of-a-gun I ever saw… an' gentle as a dead pig."

After a lengthy visit and a little more liquid supper, Slick backed his geldin' out of the trailer to show the boys. He was a tall long legged thoroughbred lookin' bay.

"Boy, this guy can cover the country," Slick started his pitch. "Only seven years old an' gentle as a dead pig."

"You already tol' me that," Billy belched as he checked the horse's teeth.

After an hour or so of Slick's sales pitch and three or four more barley sandwiches, that horse really did start to look pretty good, and Billy scrawled his name on the bottom of a check. The bay gelding was his.

"I'm gonna name him Slick," Billy slurred at his horsetradin' friend. "That way if he ain't no good ever' one will know where I got him."

"If he's not just like I told you, you don't own him," was Slick's confident reply as he rattled out of the yard. Billy ambled down to tie his new horse in the barn.

The next morning that brand new horse didn't look so good.

"That durn Slick must have doped that nag," Dick chuckled as the bay flashed a white eyeball his way and stood quivering in the stall. "….gentle as a dead pig, my foot. Only thing he's got that resembles a pig is those itty-bitty eyes. You just been rooked, Billy."

202

Billy was too proud to admit that he may have made a mistake, so he saddled him up and stepped on in the round corral behind the barn…. just in case. It sure was a good thing. Slick took off like he was shot out of a rocket, and stuck Billy's head in the dirt. Now Billy's no slouch, but that gentle-as-a-pig bay gelding bucked him off three times before he finally got him rode that mornin'. Dick could hardly contain his glee, and was thinkin' that this whole show was even better than the county fair.

Billy might be a booze hound but he isn't any quitter, and he finally got Ol' Slick where he could ride him….. at least most of the time. He spent the whole summer puttin' miles on that cayuse. His dumb pride wouldn't let him call the horse trader up and make him take the nag back. He was determined to make a horse out of him.

One evening this fall, Dick was out behind the house just finishin' up hanging some overalls on the clothesline, when he heard something coming up the lane. Billy was still out putting a few more miles on Ol' Slick, and was due back anytime.

"Sounds like a dad-blamed moter-sickle," Dick says to himself. That seemed a little strange. He couldn't remember anyone ever drivin' one in the yard before.

It was Billy. It seems he'd dropped in on one of the neighbors over across the ridge and traded ol' Slick off on that contraption. He was so glad that he'd found someone that would trade ANYTHING for that jug-headed horse that he'd forgotten the itty-bitty fact he didn't even know how to ride a motorcycle. But then, how hard could it be?

Boy, was he a sight for sore eyes. His old hat brim was blowed straight up in the front, and his batwing chaps were floppin' a tune in the breeze. He smoked right through the yard with his saddle tied on the back and made two frantic circles around the chicken coop trying to get 'er stopped.

Feathers were flying everywhere with the squawkin' old hens headed for higher ground.

"Whoa!… WHOA!…. WHOA!…. you Japanese **&%$#**," Billy yelled at his iron steed, pulling for all he was worth on the handle bars. "Look out Dick! I can't figger out how to stop this durn thing!" Dick jumped out of the way as Billy zoomed past, clipping the corner of the porch; disappearing behind the house.

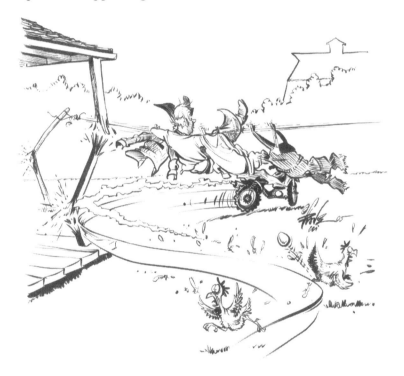

"How hard can ridin' a moter-sickle be??"

Somehow he miraculously missed both clothesline poles, but in his haste to dodge between them, Billy forgot that the clothesline was just about neck high. As a matter of fact, it was exactly Adam's Apple deep on a moter-sickled cowboy. It was an awful wreck.

Billy and his saddle wound up in a pile with Dick's wet overalls and two busted clothesline poles. The loss of its cargo didn't seem to slow down the demonic motorcycle a bit. It careened headlong another fifty yards and then crashed into the creek.

"Where'd ya get that thing, anyway?" Dick asked.

Billy untangled his head from the clothesline and spit out a tooth. "None o' yer business! If you was a real friend you'd help a fella get that dad-blamed thing strung out so I could take it back home."

Dick bit his lip to keep from laughin' out loud. There's times a fella just has to get all by himself to get really tickled, and this was one of 'em. He fished the motorcycle out of the creek and helped Billy strap his saddle back on and straighten the handlebars.

Billy wasn't sayin' much. "Just point 'er towards the gate, an' git out of the way," he grumbled. Out of the yard he roared in a cloud of smoke.

A couple of hours later, he trotted back in the yard on a big long legged bay.

"That's about the best lookin' son-of-a-gun I ever saw," Dick grinned.

"Yep," Billy grinned back, his smile freshly missing a tooth. "Gentle as a dead pig, too."

"Dad blame it, Dick. If I coulda got a hackamore
on that durn thing, I think I coulda rode 'er."

Chapter
Forty-Three

Wrong Filly Disease

I just ran into an old pard down at the NILE Livestock Show in Billings. Me 'n Earl cut quite a rug back in our day... trouble is, I don't think he ever outgrew it. He married well; I'll have to give him that. Mary Ellen grew up on a cow outfit down on the Musselshell, and Earl just sort of slid right into that deal. She's a dandy gal, and a good looker too, but how in the world she's put up with that guy all these years is beyond me.

Don't get me wrong here, Earl was a good partner to travel with. He was always right there with a dollar if you were short, and he'd dang shore hold up his end of the deal. He's a whale of a hand with a horse and a rope too, but I think bein' married to him might be sort of a challenge.

You see everybody likes Earl.... but 'specially the ladies.... and being the accommodatin' sort of a guy that he is, he always had a half a dozen of 'em on the string all the time. Although there were numerous logistical problems and more than a few broken hearts in the old days, somehow he managed to live through it. That might work out OK if you're a wild young buckaroo, but when you get fitted with your very own personal silver mounted matrimonial halter, that stuff is all 'sposed to change.

Well, then along came Mary Ellen. She was about the best lookin' gal north of the Yellowstone, and although I think she could see right through ol' Earl, I guess maybe she thought she spied something of value there that the rest of us had somehow overlooked. They've been hitched for a long time now, so it just could be that she was right.

It had been years since I'd seen them, and me 'n Earl spent a couple of days looking the cattle over, while Mary Ellen took in all of the horse clinics and sales. I'm sure she must have picked up a load of pointers that are going to come in handy down the road.

The very first day they ran into a couple of gals that had some nice looking horses there at the show, and in the bunch were a couple of dandy stud colts. Mary Ellen just fell in love with one of them, but that durn Earl couldn't seem to see anything but the lady Wranglers.

That's where they were when I happened on them. We stood around and visited some, and knowin' Earl like I do, I picked up on what was happening right away. Mary Ellen seemed totally oblivious to his wanderin' eye, and ignoring the obvious, continued to admire the colts. I don't think the horse ladies were quite as naïve…. but then they were tryin' to sell horses, and I assume they considered the situation just another one of those occupational hazards. I scooted ol' Earl off to look at the bulls, and it wasn't long until that particular set of Wranglers were completely off his mind.

Mary Ellen was really interested in one of the horses in particular, and stayed on to visit about pedigrees and such. Buster was the tall handsome young sorrel stallion she had marked in her sale catalogue, and she wanted to find out all she could about him before the sale.

"Did you remember the Vicks?" one of the horse ladies asked her partner.

"Yup, it's right here," came the answer, as her friend handed over the familiar blue jar of aromatic ointment.

"Looks like we're going to need it." Buster rolled back his top lip and pawed at the ground as he let out a squeal directed at the pretty bay mare that was battin' her eyes at him from across the alley. The experienced horsewomen gently rubbed a generous gob of the camphor and menthol laced ointment deep inside of the young stallion's nostrils, and then one of the gals took his halter rope and led him away for a little exercise.

"Sorry.... we sure hate to do that, but it's his first time in town, and all these new fillies are sort of a distraction," the owner apologized. "But, with that Vicks in his nose, he can't smell as well, and he settles right back down."

Meanwhile, Earl and I were over looking at the bulls, and missed this entire exchange. We took in the rodeo together that night and agreed to meet at the cattle sale the next day.

Early the next morning found us back at the barns again. Mary Ellen was over checking out the horses once more, and Earl and I took one final look at the cattle before the sale. Those registered livestock folks really know their business. The cattle were all groomed to perfection, and they had some of the sweetest smelling hay in front of them that I believe I've ever seen.

"Boy, just take a whiff of that hay Earl," I said, admiring the full manger.

"Won't do me a lick of good... can't smell a thing. Mary Ellen said she thought I looked like I was comin' down with a cold, and so she stuffed my nose plumb full of Vicks this mornin'."

Whatever works I guess.

"Now that'd be a tough problem to have, Billy. Us now, we got NO FILLY Disease. The last female around here's the one that followed Ol' Lucky home. No wonder he's always grinnin'."

Chapter
Forty-Four

Crippled Old Broncs
& Cowboy Softies

*I*t's sometimes hard to keep the right perspective isn't it? Getting all caught up in the normal battle of life is like fallin' off a rock. It's fairly easy. Unfortunately, I know that most of my days have been spent sort of bobbin' around like a cork in an ocean, looking for the spot to stop up the leak. What an exercise in futility. If I ever find the boss of this dang mismanaged outfit, I'm gonna quit.

I've done a little retrospective analysis, and have found that in the process of trying to maintain our idyllic, poverty-ridden, rural lifestyle, there have been a few times that I have almost destroyed the very thing I was trying to preserve. It was completely unintentional, mind you, and I'm workin' hard to get a handle on it, but frankly there are several occasions when a perspective adjustment was definitely in order. Let me explain.

The amount of work, dedication and "Blood sweat and tears" required to keep a small family agricultural operation in business certainly isn't any secret to anyone that's ever been involved with one, but it's completely beyond comprehension to anyone that hasn't. Try as they may... they just don't get it.

Pinchin' every nickel, and workin' 'til you drop are things that are just expected. Little things like bruised body parts are taken for granted.... but then as Claire Boyce was fond of saying, "It's hard to kill a cowboy".

I was about eight or ten years old when I recall getting one of my first memorable lessons in self-sacrifice. My Grandad and I were fixing some fence down through a patch of rose bushes. He had his shirtsleeves rolled up past his elbows and the thorns had his arms all scratched and bleeding. He seemed totally oblivious, and just kept pullin' wire and driving staples.

"Grandad, why don't you roll your shirtsleeves down? The stickers are scratchin' your arms all up." He was so busy getting the fence fixed that he hadn't even noticed.

"I don't want to tear my shirt. Hide 'll grow back, Boy..... shirts cost money. Hand me the pliers."

I carried on the grand tradition around here. Any wound more than a foot from your heart wasn't even considered worthy of mention. Getting the job finished was the focus, and everything else was expendable. That sure gets the work done, but there are times when the cost of the things that get expended may be a little more than we had anticipated. The realization of that fact has caused me to turn over a new leaf. I'm now taking a little more time to stop and smell the horse pucky.

The Good Lord must know that's the way some of us would operate, so he invented Grandkids. They have a way of getting away with things that their parents certainly never did, and I'm sort of pleased to say, that I'm not the only one around here that has had a perspective adjustment. It appears to happen to horses, too.

I've got an old cow horse named Benny that has really been a dandy. Back in his prime he bucked me off a few times, and a couple more he tried pretty hard but I somehow managed to get him rode. There's an awful lot of horse there, and through the years I've been pretty selective about letting anyone else ride him.

Faith, Rio Dawn, and Benny "the bronc"
When a cowgirl is mountin' a bronc, a good
hand to help comes in mighty handy.

Sadly, his prime and mine are both somewhere back on the trail someplace, and a little four-year-old brown-haired beauty named Faith has us both wrapped right around her finger. She can ride him anywhere, and when she leads him to water he puts his head down so that his nose just

213

touches her shoulder, being oh so careful not to step on her. You really wouldn't know that it's even the same horse. What a softy.

Perspective will do that, I guess. Not long ago the same little gal was with me in town. We had the gooseneck stock trailer on behind the pickup, and were buying some parts or something, when a revelation hit my little cowgirl.

"Grandad, did you know that there are treats over in that store over there?" she asked pointing towards the drugstore.

"No kiddin'?"

"No, I'm not kiddin'. Just drive over there and I'll show you." So this softy old cowboy squeezes into the drugstore parking lot, and takes up a dozen or so parking places with the pickup and trailer, and we go in the door. She knew exactly where they were, and marched right over to the candy counter and pointed, "See, I told you."

Next came a couple of fairly remarkable events. First she didn't even ask me for any candy, which in itself is extraordinary for a kid containing any of my selfish sweet toothed genetics, so I popped the question, "Would you like one of those?" indicating the candy bar at the end of her pointy finger.

"Sure! Thanks Grandad!"

I searched my pockets for a little change.... nothin'. So, I reached for my wallet and to my chagrin, the only thing in it was the fifty-dollar bill I'd been savin' for a year. Next came the second remarkable event. I actually broke that humongous bill I had stashed to buy a dad-blamed fifty-cent candy bar. I just don't understand it.... I think me 'n Benny are both turnin' into a couple of softies.

214

Chapter Forty-Five

The High Caliber Prolapse

It sure is funny how one area of the country can vary so much from another. What seems so natural to someone in their own locale is like speaking a foreign language to a newcomer. Of course, those of us that are natives around here, somehow imagine that the rest of the world thinks exactly like we do, and if they don't.... well it's just 'cause they're dumb.

Well, I'll let you in on a little secret. There really isn't anything much dumber than a country boy in the big city, either. We just as well take a felt tipped pen and write "Sucker" on our forehead, because they can see us comin' for a block.

We had some of those "foreign" city folks move in across the creek from us several years ago. Here's the way it worked: We had an extra house out here on the place that nobody was livin' in and there was a nice young family in town that had to move out of their house, and had no place to go. I didn't know them, but the little woman of the house did, and she finally convinced me that it was a good idea to rent the place to them. After all, it would only be temporary… until they found something else. Fifteen years later they were still there. I finally had to burn 'em out to get rid of them.

Now, caterin' to renters really isn't my cup of tea, so we had a little talk before they moved in. "OK, you can live there, but don't call me when the faucet starts drippin'. I won't fix the durn things in my own house, and I'm not changin' the washers on any of 'em on your side of the creek either. If you've got a problem, you're the guy that's gonna fix it." Actually it worked out about as well as a fella could ask for, and we gained some lifelong friends… even though they were "foreigners".

You see the Gilge family were city folks. Lois was a Montana gal (but a town one), and Kent was from beautiful downtown Chicago. Growing up he'd sometimes hang out over at his buddy's house… I can't remember his name, except that it was Italian. Turns out the guy's Dad was in the Mafia. It's good thing I didn't find that out before they moved in, or I would have probably put that knob back on the kitchen door that had been missing for a couple of years.

Calling Kent a town kid (even though he was) really gives folks the wrong impression of the guy. He'd spent all of his boyhood summers with relatives in rural Wisconsin, and was an avid outdoorsman. He used to dream about being just like Jim Bridger…. (I think he still does.) He'd rather fish than eat… of course, maybe that's because he was also an ardent trapper, and his boys always wanted to eat everything they caught. Muskrat stew or Rattlesnake a'la-mode were some of their favorite dishes. They always had skinless carcasses layin' all over the yard. (Maybe now you can see why I burned them out?)

They were good helpful neighbors though, even if they didn't savvy much about ranch life. "If you ever need any help with the calving when Ken's gone," Kent volunteered, "you be sure and call me."

Well sure enough, I was off playin' my guitar right in the middle of calvin' one time, and the cook had this big problem, and was in over her head.

"Quick!" she called Kent on the phone one midnight, "We've got a prolapse down in the barn! Get here as fast as you can."

The Gilges hadn't lived here all that long then, and Kent was pretty unfamiliar with that specific terminology and the extent of the problem at hand. Of course, it WAS midnight, and she'd suddenly awakened him from a wonderful dream (probably about a fight to the death between Jim Bridger and the Chicago Mafia). "Prolapse?" he thought to himself. "That's a new one." He had no idea what size of critter a prolapse was. All he knew for sure was that the neighbor lady sounded concerned, and it must need killin' quick because it was apparently in the barn bothering the animals.

"I wonder if I should take the 22 or the 12 Gauge Shotgun?" he thought to himself. "A prolapse might be as big as a badger or a coon…. Or maybe even a wolverine!" To be on the safe side he took the shotgun.

When he arrived shortly at the barn, with his boots still unlaced and only one button done on his pants, there in the dim light of the one volt flashlight, he got his very first glimpse of a genuine Montana uterine prolapse. (Boy, there's times I miss those Herefords, but that ain't one of 'em.)

217

Because some of our "foreign" city cousins might be digesting this little tale just before dinner, I'll spare you some of the more intimate details, but I must say it was bigger than a coon or a badger.... yup, about the size of a wolverine, but it didn't need shootin'. It just needed fixin'. When the poor old cow had delivered the calf, she'd gone and turned herself completely inside out.

With the help of an old retired cowboy in town that the cook had commandeered to do the needle and thread part, all she needed now was somebody that was strong as a bull, wasn't afraid of a little blood, and could take orders. (Well, two out of three isn't that bad, and Lois has him to where he follows them most of the time now.)

The two "experts" explained to our new Chicago neighbor exactly what they needed him to do, and he rolled up his sleeves and went to work.

"Well, guess I won't be needin' this," he sheepishly grinned, leaning the shotgun against the wall.

Doggone , but it sure is good to have neighbors you can count on. (If that ain't in the Bible, it ought to be.)

"Couldn't that remark about Herefords
be construed as racial profiling?"

218

Chapter Forty-Six

Hood-Winkin' the Palomino Kid

The lazy summer sun was still lingerin' high in the western sky above the Rockies as Steve and Shelly Matson limped their little Ford Fairlane into Heart Butte, Montana. Steve was a junior high teacher and had landed his very first job there at the school on the Blackfeet Reservation. The mountain air was fresh, and the scenery was breathtaking. They were so excited to get settled into their new home and community.

It's a wonder Myrtle had even made it. That's the pet name they'd hung on their old car, and she'd sure seen better days, but she had somehow managed to cough and choke and smoke her way all the several thousands of miles from their old home in Florida. I'm sure their families back home breathed a huge sigh of relief when they got the call that they'd finally made it to their destination safe and sound.

Steve was fresh out of college. He and Shelly had been married for nearly three years, and she was in the family way, expecting their first child right after Christmas. Everything they owned in the world was either in or tied to the top of old Myrtle. The little community accepted their new members with open arms, and because their Scandinavian ancestry had marked them both with a full head of nearly white blonde hair, they were instantly tagged "The Pair o' Palominos" by their neighbors.

The school year got underway, and Shelly found a doctor in Shelby to watch over her pregnancy. They were so excited as her tummy grew, and Steve got ol' Myrtle all tuned up and ready to go, and he'd time every trip they made to the doctor's office. It's a "fer piece", as my Granny used to say, from Heart Butte to Shelby and come delivery time they needed to know just how long the trip was going to take. Being one of those analytical sort of guys, Steve wanted to make sure he had 'er all under control.

There was just one little problem he hadn't thought of. It doesn't snow in Florida, and it does in Heart Butte.... boy, does it. They had their first little shot of winter in September of that year, and right away Steve could see that Myrtle just wasn't going to be something he could depend on. Especially if the snow got deep and Shelly HAD to get to the doctor in a hurry.

He really didn't have any alternative, so he financed one of those brand new four-wheel drive, SUV kind of outfits. She was a real beauty, and although the payments were a little on the steep side, they couldn't afford to take any chances. The Palomino Kid just couldn't wait until they got some REAL snow so that he could see what his new outfit could do. Myrtle needed a little rest anyway, and she could just rest up 'til spring.

He didn't have long to wait. The week before Thanksgiving, Old Man Winter decided it was time to come down out of the mountains and bless the little community with the real deal. A nice fresh 30-mph breeze and a foot of snow plugged the whole place up tight.

Not to worry. Steve was having the time of his life, charging around through the snow banks with his new toy. He instantly turned into the "Palomino Good Samaritan" by pulling stuck folks out of snow banks and jump-starting several others. No wonder the community loved him. He rounded a corner to the main road leading out of town and there stood five or six guys huddled in the cold, just looking at their car that was nearly buried in the snow on the shoulder of the road.

"Hey, Palomino. How 'bout a haaand," one of the guys yelled as Steve rolled down the window.

"Sure," was the quick answer. "You need a jump?"

"Naw. Dis car don't jump. Hafta pull 'er."

Steve wheeled in and made a track back to the front bumper of the stalled car, and one of the guys hooked up the brand new tow rope our hero had gotten just for this type of emergency.

"Just head 'er down 'at way.… to Dupuyer. Just keep goin'. It might take 'er quite a pull. She's pretty cold out, aanit?"

Steve eased to the end of the towrope, and all four of the traction tires bit into the frozen roadway. Away they went. The temperature was way below zero, and with all of those bodies inside, the windows in the stalled car fogged over solid.

With a watchful eye on his rear view mirror, Steve could see the driver of the towed car constantly wiping the condensation from the windshield. He must have pulled them at least a mile or so, and still the old car didn't start. Steve began to slow down, but the driver of the car wound down his window and motioned for him to keep going, and yelled to go a little faster.

This was repeated several times. Each time Steve would slow to see if there was something they could do to help the old car start, the window would come down again and they'd yell, "Keep goin'!"

After several miles down the road, it was obvious that the old outfit just wasn't going to start, and Steve was concerned about how cold it must be in the car he was pullin' so he eased to a stop on the shoulder, and walked back to the other vehicle.

"Did she even ever try to start?"

"Naw…. She's purty cold out, though. Aanit?"

"I don't know how we'll ever get you turned around now with all this deep snow."

"Just pull 'er on in to Dupuyer. I got a cussin there that can help us."

"Holy smoke!" Steve thought to himself, "It's another ten miles to Dupuyer." But not seeing any alternative, he pulled his frozen cargo on into the little town. They had barely rolled to a stop in front of the tavern when all the passengers baled out and made a dash for the bar. They went on inside, and Steve popped the hood on the old car.

It was no wonder it hadn't started. The engine was gone. He followed the boys into the warmth of the tavern to see what in the world was goin' on. The bottom line was they just wanted a ride to the bar, and Steve's generous nature was just what they were looking for.

"But, why didn't you tell me there wasn't any motor in that car?"

"You never axxed me that, aanit? You axxed, "Want a jump?" and I said "No… dis car don't jump…. hafta pull 'er."

"Thanx fer da pull."

This is based on a true story related to me by my friend Ike Hall. Ike is a singin' Indian cowboy that ranches on the Blackfeet Reservation. (He runs his cow herd on a percentage. He gets all of them that the Grizzlies don't eat.)

Chapter Forty-Seven

Hangin' Time?

*P*erhaps I need to apologize in advance for this little story. I'm sorry. I usually try to tell a tale that will tickle your funny bone a little. The way I figure it, life is just too dang serious, and laughin' is supposed to be good for your gizzard. I'm afraid this one isn't very funny.

You're not going to believe what happened at our place. A couple of years ago, one February evening, some sicko with a gun tied into our cowherd. We'd been feedin' them right next to the county road, and the guy just stopped his outfit on the road and apparently got out and started blazin' away.

We found two dead cows in the morning as we went down to feed. One of them had her loin steaks removed, and the other one had a big slice cut in her back on one side of the back strap. I guess something must have scared the criminal off, as he didn't finish the job on the second cow.

We've been in the cow business a long time, and this beats anything that's ever happened to us. The really sick part of this whole affair is that the cows were gut shot, and couldn't have been dead by the time the guy started cuttin' on 'em. You'd think he would have the common decency to shoot the poor old girls in the head before he started in with his knife.... nope.

One of the unfortunate vicims.

We also noticed another cow.... one of the cook's pets, that didn't look too good. We figured that she was probably gut shot, too. Sure enough, we found her and another three-year-old heifer dead a couple of days later. That made four altogether. The rest of them looked all right as far as we could tell, but he used a fairly small gun or a light load of powder, because finding a bullet hole was nearly impossible.

A surface glance would tell a casual observer that someone probably had it in for us.... perhaps settling a score for an old debt or a twisted business deal. I really don't think that's the case. I'm not too sure I have anyone that hates me bad enough to call me a dirty name, much less make some poor animals suffer to get even for something. I think it was just a random act of cruel stupidity. Our poor old cows were just in the wrong place at the wrong time. Sort of like the folks in the Twin Towers.

There is something that really disturbs me a whole lot more than the monetary loss of the cattle. Gaining the meat certainly wasn't the motive. I think that was just a little add on. The guy just wanted to watch something die, and see how many animals he could knock down in the shortest amount of time. I'm no psychologist, but it doesn't take much imagination to see this twisted mind setting up shop down by the playground to see how many little kids he can get with one clip. After all, that would be more of a challenge.... smaller target.

We have put out a $1000.00 reward. After the loss we've already taken, what's another thousand bucks? There is also a real possibility that the reward pot might be sweetened by the Montana Department of Livestock and perhaps some of the related livestock associations. This guy needs to be stopped. Who or what is next?

My heart is sick. It is probably caused by a combination of this loss, coupled with all of the terrorist business, and my frustration over the undesirable changes I see in society in general. We seem almost powerless to have much of an affect on the positive outcome of anything. Justice and righteousness seem elusive, sometimes don't they?

We certainly aren't the first to feel this way, and probably won't be the last. I recently read "The Vigilantes of Montana" by Professor Thomas Dimsdale. The Prof was a Virginia City resident, and wrote his narrative in 1865, shortly after the Vigilante cleanup. The decent citizens of that day also felt powerless against the forces of violence and crime.

Things now are a lot different, but they're also a lot the same. In that day and age, there was no law... the officers were corrupt and self-serving, and the criminals hid behind them. Now we have capable and honest law enforcement people that are hopelessly hamstrung by laws that protect the criminals. Laws that WE allowed our representatives to enact. (OJ Simpson... a good case in point.)

The Vigilantes of old took control of the situation, and cleaned the place up. No matter what your view of that is, it's pretty hard to argue with the results. It DID clean the place up. I certainly don't advocate that, and would never presume to take the law into my own hands.... so.... if someone happens to find a corpse hanging in a tree, although I definitely won't know anything about it, it surely wouldn't surprise me if a discovery like that would be the last time we hear of any wanton cow killin', and the Good Lord only knows how many kids it would save.

Editor'sNote:

Since this was written, at least partial justice has been served. Thanks to the initial investigation of Government Hunter, Gene Bucklin, and the diligence of Blaine County Deputy Sheriff, Pat Pyette, one man pled guilty to the shootings. The guilty plea was obtained primarily from DNA evidence. DNA tracers from one of the cows was a positive match for the blood found on a pair of the shooter's boots. This was the first cast EVER where DNA evidence was used in a cattle killing case.

Chapter Forty-Eight

Fast Horses, Fat Cows & Good Lookin' Women

Aahh… Montana. Where the horses are fast, the cattle are fat, and the women are all good lookin'. I was thinkin' that I should write a book about all I know about women. It ought a sell like hotcakes. Ever' guy I know would want to read something that would totally explain the complexities of the female thought process. Right?

The problem is it'd be a dang short book. I've come to the conclusion that the older I get the less I know about women. I think it was Will Rogers that said, "There are three things that cowboys will just never understand; money, racehorses, and women."

We do have more good lookin' women around here than in lots of other spots, though. Bein' an appreciator of

227

the finer things in life, lookin' at pretty girls is one of my favorite pastimes, and we seem to have a few more than our share in this part of the country.

I think it might have something to do with our larger than normal Scandinavian population. Of course if there actually is a larger percentage of good lookin' girls who can trace their ancestry to that part of the world, there's a perfectly good reason for it; Natural selection.

I sure don't need to explain what that is to anyone in the cow business, but maybe it's time for a little history lesson to illustrate my point. The Vikings of old were some pretty tough dudes. They went anywhere they wanted and did pretty much what they wanted after they got there. One of the favorite pastimes of Erik the Red and Hagar the Horrible (of comic strip fame), was to float on down to what is now the British Isles for a little R&R.

Imagine the horror that would strike the hearts of the defending force to see a half a dozen Viking ships sailing into their harbor. It seems the Norsemen liked to do that on a fairly regular basis, and rumor has it that the first time they had a real fight on their hands. Unfortunately for them, the brave defenders were no match for the fierce Vikings, and the only local men folk to survive the ensuing battle were the ones that ran like crazy for the hills.

Erik and Hagar and the boys spent a few days in town socializing with local ladies before sailing back to Oslo (or wherever they came from). Of course, "To the victor go the spoils," so the saying goes. The problem was they had more girls rounded up than would fit in the boat. Here's where natural selection comes in.

I've really never run into this problem, but trying to think like a Viking, I'm fairly certain they wouldn't waste precious cargo room on plainer looking gals. After all, they had a reputation to uphold, and certainly wouldn't want to be the laughing stock of the next Sons of Norway Convention. As a matter of fact, I would venture to say that there was probably some pretty fierce competition to see who could come home with the prettiest prizes.

They only had two itty-bitty obstacles to overcome; all the broken hearted not-so-cute damsels that were left crying on the beach, and the whuppin' that Hagar the Horrible would get after explaining the whole deal to Helga when he got back home. Viking legend has it that after the first trip into a harbor, the going got a lot easier. On the second excursion, all the men ran for the hills while the women ran toward the beach.

Here in the frigid northern snowbound sections of our country where the Scandahooovian population is fairly dense, whadaya know, but we're the happenstantial benefactors of centuries of natural selection. Thanks, Hagar.

Boy, it ain't that way ever' where else. Ken Romriell is a cowboy pal of mine from Idaho, and by the story he told me, apparently one of the descendants of the gals left on the beach lives out that way. "She's got a heart of gold, but she dang shore ain't much to look at."

I asked him to explain himself a little further, and here's the tale he told:

"There were these three cowboys that worked way up in the timber on a remote outfit. They had been pals for years, and this lady I was tellin' you about set her cap for one of 'em. She was a real nice lady, but oooowweee.... she was ugly as a sore on a sow. Charley and her tied the knot last spring and they moved on to a little place of their own several miles down the river."

"This winter, the other two boys got word that there had been an addition to the family, so Lefty offered to do all the feedin' if Pete would go on down and see the new baby and check on how the family was gettin' along. Well, that's just what happened."

229

A couple of days later Pete came riding back into camp with his report.

"The baby's healthy, and Charlie and his bride seem to be doin' just fine. She's a heck of a cook, too," Pete paused, "but that's beyond any shadow of a doubt the ugliest woman I ever saw."

"Ah, she can't be that bad."

"She dang shore is! Right after I got there the baby lit into fussin'. Reckon he musta been hungry, so his Mama threwed a blanket up over her shoulder and stuck the little shaver under there to get somethin' to eat. I never seen the like o' that…. she's so dad-blamed ugly she had to blin' fold the poor little tyke to get him to nurse."

"Now, I think that's about the most chauvinistic story I've ever heard."

Chapter
Forty-Nine

Sayonara Cowboy

*A*ahh… the life of a travelin' cowboy singer. She ain't all she's cracked up to be, I'll tell you that. I know…. I know…. most guys would probably relish the idea of trading places with one of us big-time singin' types. There's the bright lights, the big money, the limousines…. not to mention the travel to exotic places, and (of course) the girls. Girls are a real sucker for a cowboy with a guitar, you know.

I hate to bust your bubble, but most of the time none of that stuff is even remotely the truth…. except the part about the girls. I've got a real knack for impressin' girls. The one little problem I have so far is that they're either under 10 or over 90. Those two age groups seem to think I'm great, but the ladies in between just don't appear to be all that awe struck. That one still needs a little work, and when I get it figured out I ain't tellin' a soul the secret.

There are times I've been stuck trying to entertain some of the most stuffed-shirted city types you ever saw. Boy, I'll tell you what, that's a lot of work. One of the worst times I can remember was at a pre-legislature party. We were out of state for this big doin's, and all of the lawyer/politician types were buzzin' around trying to cut some of those under the table deals, and consequently took a real dim view of this dumb one-eyed-hick cowboy making all that noise right in the same room. It was awful.

Then there's the stage. The smallest stage I ever had to work on was eight by twelve.... inches. No sir, that's the truth. I was standing on top of a railroad tie fence post in Arizona. Not much room to dance around on one of those, I'll tell you what.

One of the best singin' cowboy tales I can think of happened to a friend of mine that was hired to entertain a group of Japanese businessmen. They had been graciously flown over here in an attempt to bilk them out of a huge amount of investment capital for something or other, and their hosts wanted them to experience the true flavor of the American West by providing a genuine singin' cowboy for their listening pleasure.

There were a couple of fairly major problems. They had, of course, the obvious cultural and language barriers to overcome, but the greatest obstacle of all was the fact that the poor would-be entertain-ees hadn't been to bed for two or three days straight, were at least 150 time zones away from home, and had been plied with all the illicit liquids their hosts could pour down them since landing in our fair land. When that was added to the fact that they had also been unceremoniously ripped from their usual scant fish and rice diet, and force fed a T-bone steak the size of a Cadillac hub cap, disaster was only a matter of time.

What better tune to entertain these foreign visitors and give them a taste of the real West could there possibly be than "Little Joe, the Wrangler?" Our cowboy hero launches into his very best rendition, and upon the finale when poor Little Joe gets run over by the herd of stampeding long-horns... they just sat there and looked at him through bleary and blood-shot oriental eyes.

Stan Howe
The Sayonara Cowboy

Of course they hadn't understood a thing, and had no way of knowing that this was the end of the song. Oriental folks are probably the most well mannered people on earth, but they didn't clap or acknowledge the performance at all. They didn't have a clue.

Enter the interpreter. She was a pretty Japanese lady that spoke very good English. She stood before the crowd and spoke to them in their native tongue for several minutes, after which they clapped po-litely... twice.

"What did you tell them?" the frustrated cowboy asked. (Please excuse my lousy Japanese accent.)

"I tell dem.... Liddo boy, wi funny shoe... he ridey into kawboy camp. He wany be kawboy, too. Big kawboy, he givey liddo boy job riddy after kowboy horses. Big stomy night... veddy dark...an caddo dey get veddy scared. Dey

233

runny 'way and Liddo Joey try to stop 'em. He runny veddy fast on de veddy fastest o' da kawboy's horses, and get in front of caddo… but horsey he fa down and liddo kawboy, he get steppyed on by all da caddo. Beddy sad stody. Liddo kawboy…. he die, and big kawboys dey all beddy sad."

"Not bad," thought the singer to himself. "I couldn't have told that any better myself."

For the second tune to further enrich the visitor's cultural experience, our friend begins the old cowboy classic, "Ghost Riders In The Sky." At the conclusion, the story was the same. The audience again looked at him in polite silence until the pretty interpreter once more took command of the microphone, and spent several minutes explaining the song to them in Japanese. At the end of her explanation they again clapped politely…. twice.

"It's going to be a long night," our entertainer friend thought to himself, as he launched into another old time Western favorite, giving it his very best. He was again greeted by polite silence, and once more the attractive interpreter took the microphone. This time it only took her a half a dozen words to explain the entire song, and the crowd went absolutely wild. They clapped, they cheered, and they held their sides, laughing hysterically.

"What did you tell them?" asked our rugged man of the West.

"I tell dem this is veddy nice song about kawboy. Dis kawboy getty on veddy bad horse dat bucky down poor kawboy an he landy on da groun', and…."

"Come on…. tell me what you really said," the entertainer interrupted, not for a moment believing her explanation. The interpreter looked down at her shoes, her pretty flushing cheeks revealing her obvious embarrassment.

"OK….." she answered haltingly. "…. I tell dem… laff like crazy. Maybe he quit."

234

Chapter Fifty

The Las Vegas Strip

*H*ere it was over a month after the big deal, and Dick was still down in the dumps and walkin' around with this bummed-out frown on his face. He looked a lot like a sheepherder that just got his dog shot.

"Aw come on cheer up," his ol' buddy Billy chided, trying to hold back the little giggle that always seemed to sneak up out of his belly when he thought about it. "You'll pr'obly never see her again anyway."

"Just clam up," Dick snarled back, ignoring his chuckling pardner. "I'm goin' ridin'."

As soon as Dick had stomped across the kitchen and slammed the door, Billy just couldn't hold it back anymore. With his ol' buddy finally out of earshot, he broke out in a big belly laugh just thinkin' about it; so tickled that the tears were rolling down his stubbly cheeks.

You see, Dick and Billy, those two old bachelor cowboys that ranch way down by the river, had made another trip to the National Finals Rodeo in Las Vegas last fall. They'll probably go back again sometime, but right now Dick swears that he'll never set foot in that town again. "'Cause it'd be just too durn embarrassin'."

Billy popped the top on yet another liquid refreshment, and reared back in his chair to relive the moment. He'd had the time of his life.

There's a lot going on in Las Vegas when the NFR is in town, and a hick country boy can get in trouble without even tryin'. The boys had bought some brand new shirts and overalls, had sold a couple of old dry cows for a little extra money, and off to the big doin's they went.

They had quite a time too, but being a couple of buckaroo bachelors from out in the sticks that knew a whole lot more about cows and horses than about the female members of their own species, it took them a while to get the hang of things. In fact, I'm not too sure they ever did.

They went to the rodeo the first night they got there, and I'll tell you what, she was a dandy. After the big show, the boys headed back to their glitzy hotel down on the strip to see what else they could find. They soon found out that a feller could find just about anything he was lookin' for down there and a whole lot of stuff he wasn't. There were lights flashin' and bands playing and action every place.

"Boy, I'd sure like to do a little dancin'," Dick remarked, as the Texas Swing band in the crowded lounge struck up an old Bob Wills tune.

"Me too," slurred his partially inebriated partner. "But I ain't lookin' forward to getting' the dickens pounded out of me fer askin' the wrong gal to dance. How's a feller s'posed to know what's what around here?"

236

Their dilemma was soon solved when they saw an ad for female escorts. Because Dick is a better talker, Billy made him do the callin'.

"Hello. We was readin' yer ad and we're in town here for the rodeo, and we'd like to see about a couple of gals to go dancin'." There was a long pause as the lady on the other end of the phone filled Dick in on all of the details.

"Five hundred dollars! A piece? We don't want to buy 'em, we just want to dance with 'em." Dick held his hand over the receiver. "Billy this is a dumb hair-brained idea you got! They want us to pay 'em five hundred dollars a piece just to go dancin'! Fer that much money they oughta let us take 'em back t' the ranch!"

"Well," Billy burped, "I really doubt if they'll let us take 'em home fer that, but ask 'em if they know how to dance. Heck, this only comes around once a year. I don't mind tradin' that pot bellied old cow I sold fer a night o' good dancin'. I say if they know how to dance let's just go fer it."

Dick just stared at his pardner for a second or two and then took his hand off the receiver and made the deal. About a half an hour later they met the two dancin' girls in the hotel lobby, and headed down the street to where they'd heard the band playin'.

Doggone it, but those gals were friendly; a couple of real fancy thoroughbreds. They were a little on the long legged side, and their dresses might have been a little too tight and maybe just a tad too short, but then the boys reasoned with legs that long, maybe they'd sort of grown out of 'em.

They danced the night away, and had themselves a time. For some reason the girls kept lookin' at their watch and wondering if the boys wanted to go back to the hotel.

"Are you kiddin?" Billy wondered out loud. "I ain't heard a band this good since I seen old Bob Wills hisself down in Fort Worth."

The problem arose when they headed out for the pickup to go to another dancehall down the strip. Dick, bein' the athletic showoff that he is, got himself in a real pickle that he won't live down for quite a while. He told Billy and the gals to just wait out in the street in front of the casino, and he'd go back and bring the pickup around to give them a ride.

The problem was, when he cut across a little piece of grass to where the outfit was parked, there was a ten foot high security fence between him and where he needed to go. He could see his pickup over there not fifty yards away, and it was either walk all the way back around or just shinny over the fence.

Well, shinny over he did, but he ran into an itty-bitty problem. There must have been some poison in all of those refreshments they'd consumed while they'd been dancin', because he lost his balance right as he went over the top. His brand new overalls hung up on the top wire, and there he was, hanging upside down with his head five or six feet off the ground.

"Now what in the dickens am I gonna do?" Dick thought to himself. Try as he may, he couldn't wiggle free, and those new overalls weren't about to give up. There he hung.... and there was no gettin' loose. It was in a fairly dark isolated area, with not a soul to help. He was just plain stuck there.

That's when he got the bright idea. "I know! I'll just undo the buckle on my jeans and slip right out of 'em. Then I'll climb back up and unhook 'em and put 'em back on."

By rights, that does sound like a plausible remedy, but he ran into a little hitch. When he undid his jeans, he only slid about three feet further down, until his boots hung up in the legs.

238

Now, he's in even worse shape than before. His BVDs got caught in his jeans, and his shirttail is up around his neck. Now he's hangin' upside down with his shirttail covering his head and naked as a J Bird from his hocks all the way down to his armpits.

That's where Billy and the two girls found him. For some reason, the girls didn't even seem to be embarrassed by such a sight, but poor ol' Dick sure was. Fortunately the pounding in his head was loud enough he couldn't hear their giggles.

"Just think, Muffy," one of the dancin' girls giggled to the other, "we haven't seen anything like that since we saw ol' Bob Wills himself down in Fort Worth."

"To tell ya the truth, I think ya look better upside down with yer head covered up."

239

The Tailgate

Well, doggone it but maybe it's time we went back to work. A fella can't stand around tellin' stories all day long. A guy told me not long ago that "Shootin' the Breeze" just may be about as much fun as a fella can have legally. Thanks for stopping by. I sure hope you've enjoyed the B.S. as much as he did.

These little stories and all of the traveling we do across the country with our cowboy music have certainly gained us a lot of new friends. We're thankful for that, and I sure appreciate all of the encouragement.

Here is a little portion of a letter we got not long ago. It sorta makes putting all of these little yarns down on paper worth the effort. This may be the best compliment a fella can get. The letter went like this:

"I've taken your book to bed with me the last couple of nights and laughed myself to sleep both of them. As a senior citizen, I can hardly remember the last time I had this much fun before falling asleep….."

I'm not sure the flattery can get much better than that. Thank you Ma'am, and thank YOU again for taking the time out to read "Shootin' the Breeze".

Keep Smilin'.....
    and don't forget to check yer cinch.

Ken

Ken Overcast and his wife Dawn are at home on their ranch on Lodge Creek in Northcentral Montana. Ken is also a syndicated columnist, author, and recording cowboy singer. His syndicated radio program, "The Cowboy Show" is aired nationally, and he's been the recipient of many national awards including the Will Rogers Award from the Academy of Western Artists.

www.kenovercast.com

240